Connection is a Song

Connection is a Song

Coming Up and Coming Out
Through the Music of the '90s

ANNA DOBLE

NINE
EIGHT
BOOKS

NINE
EIGHT
BOOKS

NEB 025

First published in the UK in 2024 by Nine Eight Books
An imprint of Black & White Publishing Group
A Bonnier Books UK company
4th Floor, Victoria House, Bloomsbury Square, London, WC1B 4DA
Owned by Bonnier Books, Sveavägen 56, Stockholm, Sweden

@nineeightbooks

@nineeightbooks

Hardback ISBN: 978-1-7887-0948-4
eBook ISBN: 978-1-7887-0949-1
Audio ISBN: 978-1-7887-0950-7

A CIP catalogue record for this book Prelimis available from the British Library.

Publishing director: Pete Selby
Editor: James Lilford

Cover design by Jake Cook
Typeset by IDSUK (Data Connection) Ltd
Printed and bound in Great Britain by Clays Ltd, Elcograf S.p.A

1 3 5 7 9 10 8 6 4 2

Every reasonable effort has been made to trace copyright-holders of material reproduced in this book. If any have been inadvertently overlooked, the publisher would be glad to hear from them.

Nine Eight Books is an imprint of Bonnier Books UK
www.bonnierbooks.co.uk

MIX
Paper | Supporting
responsible forestry
FSC
www.fsc.org   FSC® C018072

For my parents, who gave me music – and Frankie,
who has all this to come

It was only a song
A stranger's refrain
That glanced off her heart
More flicker than flame.
She lost half the words
In the long grass of time
Yet melody clings
To the rhythm and rhyme.
It cut her and healed her
Like a honey-dipped knife
It was only a song
But the song changed her life.

Andrew Doble

Contents

Prologue

1989. A ponytailed kid stands in a North Yorkshire school hall, next to the wall bars, noticing the smell of dust. She is ten and shy. It is lunchtime, but the girl is too nervous to eat. Picked out for being underweight, her mum cuts her sandwiches into star shapes. Her best friend invites her round for tea but, wary of the awkward clink of someone else's cutlery, she says no. At the lunchtime disco, she feels every song but doesn't dare to dance.

1999. The girl has cropped, wannabe Elastica hair. She is twenty. A Marlboro Light dangles from her mouth. She's racking up tunes in the DJ booth, grinning. Adidas feet. Richey Manic eyeliner. Bands to save us, others declared dead. CDs ejected from the window into the cold Leeds night. A bag of chips, a pint of cider and a 2 a.m. epiphany.

*

I am busy reading New Kids on the Block lyrics when the first glimpses of the 1990s flicker into my peripheral vision. I am at an intersection between football and pop: an unusual crossroads for a girl at that time. I play on the left wing for my junior school team.

The only girl, the Castle School boys stand by me when opponents sneer. In between matches, I collect Panini football stickers as my older sister Claire pieces together Kim Wilde's face in her *Smash Hits* album. I am chasing elusive 'shinies' while she is holding out for a semi-naked Prince. With good timing, I switch allegiance to pop music just when the local newsagent starts filling its shelves with boys in bowl cuts and girls with guitars.

I find myself staring, bewitched, at the Manic Street Preachers in thick eyeliner with fringes held aloft by cola hairspray, and I can't work out whether they are boys or girls. I take off my shin pads and start down a new path, fighting through the brambles of Stock, Aitken and Waterman, distracted for a time by neon-pink cassettes, but soon I am in a clearing with They Might Be Giants and Blur. In my room, surrounded by the toys of childhood, I have found an escape tunnel. Pre-internet, this is it – a private space of hope and imagination; magazines, tapes, the flutter of a poster unstuck by summer air. The teen bedroom, the original place of self-invention. In mine, I begin to live in my own skin, daring to seek devotions I know exist but can't yet touch. My room becomes a refuge from the suffocating mainstream. I don't cry when Diana dies. My dream date isn't Ross from *Friends*. I'm travelling through songs that seem to answer life's pressing questions: Who do you think you are? What time is love? Why does my heart feel so bad?

1

All the flowers

Two days before the start of the 1990s, I turn eleven. December 29: a stupid birthday, lost in the haze between Christmas and New Year. It is a time of Twiglets underfoot and missing Lego pieces. I am kneeling by the fire, my elbows on the low coffee table, a glue pot and brush in my hands as I carefully construct a matchstick house. Sparks are spitting onto the hearth. I shift to avoid them and watch flecks of ash spin gently into the air. My model is a perfect little home, big enough for a sparrow, with a door in the middle and symmetrical windows. It has a little backyard, pretend paper flowers and a matchstick fence.

My sisters buy me suspiciously festive birthday presents from the Woolworths sale: foil-wrapped chocolate snowballs and a blue furry pencil case, still with a Santa tag. I don't mind all that much because while the glue is drying on each new wall of my little house, my nose is in the *Shoot!* annual given to me by my granny, Nanny Connie. She's the person in my family who sees how much I love football. I'm completely thrilled when she gifts me my Liverpool scarf that used to belong to her brother, Uncle Doug.

I'm left-footed and a winger, like my hero John Barnes. My teammate Nigel – a short, nippy little forward, always in black-and-white Newcastle United socks – says he can identify me by my shadow alone: a halo of curls at the front, a swishing ponytail at the back. This means he can pass to me without looking, and me back to him. I spin and nudge in my boots from Mardo, the discount store on the high street. I live for the thrill of delivering a perfect cross and I love the circular stencils of dried mud that fall from my studs the next day.

My new annual has England striker Gary Lineker on the cover and its pages preview the summer's World Cup in Italy, which England are going to win. I am otherwise unaware of the sporting and musical bounty – and danger – that lies ahead, but squinting through the fog of late December, across pages of shiny thighs and gelled hair, I catch a time when I will fall for Gary, his teammates and their soundtrack. This is the year I will be slide-tackled by pop music. It is also the year I will sing until I lose my voice for men with mullets in dark blue shorts.

*

The football gene is a surprise to my parents. My dad is all about music. His vinyl collection starts on the floor and stretches to the ceiling in the corner of the living room. His tall, expensive speakers have deadly carpet spikes to keep them steady and we older sisters dare each other to put a finger beneath the cold metallic point. Dad listens to American blues and European folk, and he teaches us three girls to love songs that absolutely nobody is singing in school: Serge Gainsbourg's 'Couleur Café' and Leonard Cohen's 'Bird on a Wire'. To thrill us more, he plays Clannad's *Robin Hood*

ALL THE FLOWERS

Christmas 1984, my left-handed ukulele playing style – and boredom, seemingly – already in evidence. One of Dad's speakers can be seen behind my older sister Claire as we attempt to play carols for Uncle Peter. (Photo: Peter Doble)

soundtrack so loud that the room shakes, Mum's blue-and-white china wobbling on the dresser.

We sit directly under the pulsing nylon gauze and let the vibrations pass through us, imagining we are inside the songs. *Rahh-bin, the hooded man.* My mum comes in with a look of concern, mostly on behalf of our neighbours, but they never seem to say anything, at least, not to us. Mum loves music too, but she is often busy stitching up the holes in our tights or making a stew in the kitchen. During one holiday, in a moment of betwixtmas anarchy, she takes the entrails of the Christmas day trifle, bundles it into her food mixer, then serves it to us in cold, mysterious ice-cream scoops. Nobody realises it's a pudding reborn.

We live in Knaresborough, a small market town in North Yorkshire with a ruined castle and a river. Our house, on a tall Victorian terrace, is in the centre, a three-minute walk from the shops. This later brings advantages – the sweaty run to school, the drunk scamper home from the pub – but for now it means we are likely to be sent on errands to Spar, the nearest supermarket. It's usually me, the sporty one, running through the wind tunnel – an odd local weather phenomenon – at the top of our street, returning out of breath but with a block of cheese.

In our Christmas living room, Swedish elves called Tomte men dance in red and green from hand-made wall hangings. Mum is a fan of all things old European, of mountain paths and wooden skis, the Moomins and mysterious forests. In the winter months, our house is a Scandinavian theme park: wooden reindeer, candles and the phrase 'God Jul' ('Merry Christmas' in Swedish). Mum loves nature and identifies different garden birds from their distant song. She also teaches all three of us to sew, setting us up with patterns and colour schemes. She untangles our bobbins patiently, helping us in turn. We are four years apart, and so she moves from Claire, with her mid-teen dexterity, to Kerstin, who is six and still using a giant plasticky cross-stitch grid. I find my way in the middle. I'm one of the older ones when it suits me, a little one when that has more obvious benefits. Really, I just want to stitch a footballer, but for now it's an elf.

*

On New Year's Eve, the last day of the decade, I am watching *Cilla's Goodbye to the '80s* on my parents' television set, which is angled towards the sofa on its smooth casters. It feels indestructible, this TV, with its wooden side-panels and thin rectangular buttons in dark silver. Clunk, the news. Clunk, *Top Gun* on ITV. Clunk, it's Cilla Black at the London Palladium asking us to bid farewell to the decade of *Dallas* and Mrs Thatcher. I am making my matchstick model of a perfect tiny home as the clock ticks to midnight. Its foundations sit on a cross-shaped piece of paper carefully cut along dotted lines, then folded and fortified with cardboard tabs. The kit comes with a little snipping tool that lets me trim the matches to just the right length, which is important around the windows and eaves. The glue is causing me problems, though, because it's too wet and making the walls bend. Later it's too dry and peels away like skin. Mulled wine is being passed over my head in French goblets as I try to add the chimney.

We laugh as we wave goodbye to Cilla and the sequins of a receding decade.

*

I'm trying to rescue my model house again as my big sister's friend Sula stands by the kitchen door, the cat's bowls clinking by her fidgeting foot. Sula is waiting for Claire to come downstairs, filling time by chatting to me about what she describes as the cold, empty feeling of this strange part of the year, the limbo days. We are bathed in the white glow of the fairy lights at the window, soon to be packed away, and the trailing sadness in her voice makes me stop fiddling with my house. Sula says there's nothing to look forward to as she looks down at her shoes. When Claire re-appears, she squints at us both, intrigued – and suspicious – about her friend speaking so seriously with me, a kid. They are both sixteen; I am just eleven. The conversation hangs briefly and then Claire and Sula go out. I walk slowly up two flights of stairs to my room in the loft.

A song catches me on the radio. I am in the middle of being swept away by it as Mum calls me back down for tea. The voice is pleading, and the singer sounds wounded. Whoever she is, she sounds angry, her voice a primal howl from a place of distress. She can't stop the lonely tears from falling but her tone suggests she might also punch anyone who asks why. I recognise something from my dad's records – she's a folk singer – but the sky-sized keyboards, like glimpses of blue between stratus clouds, tell me that this is no campfire tune. Drums like boulders are shunted by the weight of violin currents in the ocean. I hear a requiem for something important that is gone, and there's a bird without a song. A spirit woman rises through salt water to deliver this message. She is Sinéad O'Connor.

Released on 8 January, 'Nothing Compares 2 U' spends most of February at the top of the chart, its waves crashing through the dawn of the year, its tides taking me to new seas. I hear it again in Superdrug on the high street. It sneaks up on me from a van with its window open as I walk to school. I leap to turn up the volume when it's played on TFM (a Teesside radio station that I can pick up more clearly than local stations up in my room). I see her, the singer, at the end of *Top of the Pops*; her tearful eyes so mesmerising.

O'Connor's song casts a sorrow beam across the doorstep of the decade, this new decade: the 1990s. Is it a portent of things to come for me? The addictive qualities of very sad music? I tune in as often as I can because I'm already in love with the way this song makes me *feel*. I find myself bingeing on its melancholia, wanting it to do me emotional damage. Like Sula again at the back door, talking to me as if I am an adult, I don't understand grown-up desolation, but as I step into Sinéad's lonely glow – with all the flowers that you planted, mama – I know already, here and now, that whatever happens with people, music will never let me down. I set off down a small path covered in frozen leaves. On closer inspection, the leaves are the lyric pages from *Smash Hits*, ripped into shreds.

*

I ask for my pocket money on Saturday mornings, just after our various hairdressing needs have been met. My mum ties Kerstin's blonde hair into two sprightly bunches before moving onto my ponytail which she weaves into a plait. We are playing Bamboozle! on Teletext while all this happens, which at least keeps us still, although Kerstin is fiddling with her purple mood ring. Mum is always juggling tasks, up a ladder changing a lightbulb one minute, stirring porridge the next. She sends me off to fetch her brown leather purse that is tucked inside her handbag in the hall and then roots around for a pound coin and a fifty-pence piece. I have a subscription to *Roy of the Rovers* from Greaves' newsagent on the corner of the market place and pick up my new comic fortnightly on Saturdays, watching the shopkeeper's fingers work through the alphabet towards my name with nervous anticipation, because sometimes it's late. When I get my hands on its glossy pages, I'm so happy. No matter the injuries and attempts at sabotage, things always seem to work out for fictional team Melchester Rovers.

I follow the real football season via little tabs on a triangular cardboard league table and at school I am chasing metallic club badges for my sticker album, swapping duplicates in playground deals. When I'm caught trading them in class, Mrs Dickinson confiscates my stash indefinitely: a disaster. I reveal my Panini grief to my friend Kevin, who sits opposite me by the tall Victorian window that you can only open with a pole. We're flicking bits of paper towards each other across the table, pencils for goalposts, when he hatches his plan to help me steal my stickers back, one by one. It's not my usual style – I'm far too obedient – but the harsh length of the sentence has left me with little choice, and in the middle of the season too. I steal back the Liverpool shiny, the red Liver birds glinting at me from the darkness of the cupboard.

Claire, my older sister, is in a different sticker scene. She's long swapped the Garbage Pail Kids with their sickly pink gum for rows of pop stars with shimmering *Smash Hits* hair. Through her, I spy another universe. Also around this time a dancing epiphany happens in a garage. It's my friend Katie's birthday and her party takes place among giant white fridge units filled with milk bottles, because her dad is the local milkman. Beams of light move across the fridges as Bananarama, Kylie and Madonna echo from the breeze-block walls. There are fizzy drinks in yoghurt pot containers with pink and green ring-pulls: cola, cherry, lemonade. And in this refrigerated room, wrapped in a blanket of loud pop music, I dare to dance.

A few days later, I am sitting on the two steps up to the landing, desperately seeking my big sister's approval. I drag my cassette player outside the bathroom door as Claire is trying to get ready and play my latest Jason Donovan tape through the closed door. I am hoping to hear a grunt of appreciation, now that I am also a music fan, but it doesn't come. Claire, with her Björk tapes and dark eyeshadow is busy – and a little bit baffled – as I go searching for my own turf, still perforated by stud marks. I persevere and swap Roy Race for my own copy of *Smash Hits*. There are broken hearts and hands on hearts. I also see singers with well-washed hair on the *Chart Show*, forever glancing across the street, forlornly and in slow motion. After Sinéad, I am on my guard for sorrow. As ice rivulets appear at my slanting winter window, the always-cold loft air making me shiver, I hear a new song.

There is an electrical well, blue canaries, bees, bonnets and a magic birdhouse. A jumbled dream of words, they feel like popping candy on my tongue. I taste the vowels. I smell the newness, a gloss of silky pages in a new book. 'Birdhouse in Your Soul'. What does it mean? Something about childhood, the feeling of being half-awake. I am sitting cross-legged on my green-and-white duvet, lemon-white light streaking through the skylight, trying to crack a new code. As the song plays, I follow the riddle with my finger, across the page, my brow furrowed. It seems to be a song written from the viewpoint of a child's night light, a glowing friend. This bird, I think, is a picture illuminated by the light, or within the light, and it watches over the song's protagonist – and therefore me – as she sleeps.

A brass interlude blares like a traffic jam as the song layers over itself, a stomping grown-up nursery rhyme. They Might Be Giants, a band of two men, both called John, seem to be speaking to me in US college tongues, and as they do – with a supporting cast of whistles, bells, shipwrecks and guardian angels – I forward-roll into the nerd enclave of an American high school. I'm standing in math block, folders in my arms like in the movies, trying to look nonchalant. I'm the geek trying not to be seen. I'm the girl who might be beautiful behind big glasses. I'm the one trying to write poems on the inside of my locker. No more songs by actors from

CONNECTION IS A SONG

Neighbours. The Johns even announce their plan: *after killing Jason off and countless screaming* . . . Australians? The song is so short that it feels like a dream. I must wait to tape it from the radio and make it mine. In the future, I will hear the bounce of its opening notes even when it's not there, an echo of its opening stampede in the outros of other songs.

The matchstick house is my birdhouse. When it falls apart, I keep the paper flowers.

2

Staring at clouds

As the first spring of the decade tries to force its way through the cold, I am staring at fast-moving clouds through the loft window and listening to my hand-me-down silver cassette-radio with its old hi-fi smell. Through the pinks and yellows of a tissue-paper Beatles cover, 'Strawberry Fields Forever', with its faint echo of the 1960s, I both hear and smell the sunny skin of the decade to come. The music is saying: June is out there, hang on.

The problem is that it's freezing in my room as the wind whistles in around the chimney breast. Sometimes I pull my duvet from the bed and sculpt it around my legs and feet while I sit on the carpet, poised to hit 'record'. Around the top of the house, where I share the loft room with Kerstin, the wind howls, almost shockingly, in spiralling witchy voices, as if urging each other to new destructive deeds. Rock the chimney pots! Clatter the tiles! Snatch away the song, crunch it up!

There's a picture of the 1988 Charity Shield-winning Liverpool squad stuck up with tape on the side of my wardrobe. I look at it sideways from my pillow. Bruce Grobbelaar, the moustachioed keeper, dressed in green, grins from the back row. John Barnes smiles handsomely at the front as he crouches, slightly apart from the other players. Some of the team wear scarves handed to them by fans. Steve McMahon is in a goofy red-and-white flat cap. Barnes seems cooler than them and, in a few months, I'll know why. These footballers and their glories compete with Boris Becker on the wall above my bookshelf, where the sticky corners of my posters make the paintwork peel.

Becker is the current Wimbledon champion, introduced to me by Mum who is trying to steer me towards the genteel world of tennis. I know she is slightly worried by my fake Liverpool FC shorts, with their unnecessary supportive crotch, bought for me in the end by Nanny Connie because Mum kept saying no. Their nylon swish makes me feel like a real footballer. Mum's keenness for tennis leads me to paint a watercolour of Becker in victory pose, his finger pointing to the sky. I send it in an envelope to 'Boris Becker, Leimen, Germany' and, to my complete astonishment, and many months later, a letter marked 'Luftpost' plops onto our doormat. Inside, holy relics: two signed postcards and a note from Boris's mum. Becker takes over my walls.

On my floor is a dusty Lego castle, which opens down the middle with a hinge so that you can peer inside its rooms like a doll's house. It's been there forever, but I'm still proud of it and can't seem to bring myself to break it up. It is made with bricks from the '70s and '80s, a donation from a neighbour, and so the people have those strange, fixed arms and no faces. But I've combined them with newer sets that afford me arrow slits and pretend billowing flags. I know it's the last Lego model I will make.

On Kerstin's side, there are Kylie Minogue posters and Barbie dolls. She is messy and I am tidy, and so our room is oddly divided along these lines. The stairs come up the middle, a natural border. On my side, a neat row of shoes and clothes folded over the banister. On hers, My Little Pony accessories strewn across the green carpet. She has a toy called a Swan Keyper, a lockable plastic bird with bright pink wings, a purple beak and dramatic nylon hair. Unkindly, I pick the keyhole and leave random spooky messages inside. When Mum wants to get us down for dinner, we are so far away, at the top of the house, that she rings an old school bell.

Our shared space is still crammed with toys. Along the sides, under the eaves, there are long cupboards filled with inaccessible childhood treasure. We can't fully open the doors because our beds block their path. 'A stupid design,' Mum says under her breath, still cross with the loft man, as we search for a board game. It means we can only access our things at the top end, leading to funny but frustrated scenes when we want something that's *at the other end*. I send in Kerstin, aged seven, smaller and nimbler, with a skipping rope around her waist. Like a Victorian chimney sweep, she scrabbles into the darkness and returns, hoisted back into the light a few cobwebby minutes later, triumphant, with the Monopoly box.

*

As the winter thaws, the strawberry song comes with me. The soft fruits of summer beckon. I'm listening to my radio tape of incomplete songs. Depeche Mode's 'Enjoy the Silence', interrupted by Bruno Brookes. Technotronic's 'Get Up (Before the Night is Over)', blighted by a jingle. Candy Flip's 'Strawberry Fields Forever', with a clunking noise at the start. As I lean back on my bed, unfolding my body into the first warmth of the year, I experience a light and airy sensation. Swimming, descending piano chords and a near-whispered vocal fill my ears. Nothing is real. In the skylight's reflection, my cheeks turn white and gold as the sun shifts across the glass. Without looking down, I cross my arms and gently touch each shoulder to check that I am still here. Fuzzy pianos and shuffling house beats reach me in shifting pastel colours. A cheap, fake little trumpet circles the outro as the clouds through the window change shape. Only the crumple of my elbow in the *Smash Hits* centrefold breaks the spell.

I'm a pop fan now. Tapes, stickers, badges. *Pop Shop* always comes with a free tape. This week, Neneh Cherry, Salt-N-Pepa and Wop Bop Torledo. Magazines are the internet of spring 1990 and everyone's skin is very smooth, but soon there will be scruffy boys with spots, like the real world: the Beloved, the Farm and EMF. I'm still in the strawberry field when I find myself bewitched by a poster of the Manic Street Preachers with their big eyes and felt-tipped words of despair.

Candy Flip's light-dappled quilt rolls me off my bed and into an imaginary meadow. It is deliciously lightweight: a cute, stoner reworking with synthetic strings that taste like Opal Fruits. My dad is appalled. He grew up in Liverpool and has stories of the real Beatles and the *real* Cavern Club. He loves the original rhythm and blues, folk and country music. The music he chooses is earthy and authentic: of grass, mud and mountains. He tells us about the legendary songwriting duos, from Bacharach and David to Goffin and King. We listen to him, willing sponges for musical information, but our attention is stolen back by lip-syncing pop stars in foil tops and sportswear, by Betty Boo and groovy trains. A secret lyricist

14

himself (with a chart song to his name),[i] Dad comes into the living room to wistfully observe music's downfall on *Top of the Pops*.

The singer is wearing baggy blue jeans and an oversized geometric-patterned jacket. It slips from his shoulders as he moves his arms, revealing a glimpse of raver pendant. Not only is his candyfloss vocal an insult to John Lennon but he's miming too – and badly. The keyboardist sways in a striped top behind his synthesiser, not really playing the notes, and the backing singers shake maracas lazily, like Ian Brown at Spike Island, if I knew what Spike Island was. It is knowingly bone-idle and I absolutely love it. Somehow the song's nothingness makes me feel weightless and free, a premonition of the mood of opportunity that the decade will bring.

My parents watch TV news every night and talk all the time about politics. Mrs Thatcher is referred to as *that woman*. The label comes from my elderly aunts, Ida and Winnie, who live in an elegant mansion in Harrogate – surely a Thatcher heartland, but no. Like Macbeth, saying the prime minister's name out loud is deemed unwise by them and so that woman becomes a family joke that we repeat but don't fully understand. I overhear that yuppy culture is over. Big hair is out, bowl cuts are in. George Harrison's sitar has seemingly been acquired from a hidden section of the Argos catalogue where incense and chunky beads are also for sale; a new breed of hippie is here, with a fag behind the ear and a fairground earring. I watch the *Six O'Clock News* and see a report about ravers being chased by police.

I don't know yet about chemical nights, but the charts are filling with dance music, bundled off the motorway slip-road and into the

---

[i] 'Cavern of Dreams'/'England in my Hands', Pete Rimmer/Andrew Doble (1984).

shops where I go. Nobody notices that 'candy flipping' is a slang term for mixing ecstasy with acid, and that includes me. In my bedroom, the light fades. I smooth out the creases on the page and look for more lyrics about fruit.

*

Music fills our house in layers. The distant buzzing crowd of a Radio 1 roadshow moves through the top third. In the middle, where the bathroom is, my older sister Claire's ghetto blaster reigns supreme: All About Eve, Carly Simon and Prince. Downstairs in the living room is the tall wooden unit by the door that's home to hundreds of my dad's LPs. We only recognise the names of a few artists: Abba, Bob Dylan, Dusty Springfield. Dad knows who wrote what, when and on which record label it was released. Mum sits down with us to watch the new top ten, mostly to laugh at the hairstyles.

My school has an indoor vineyard running down a slope to the haunted toilets. On the way to assembly in the main hall, we reach up to steal little blue grapes. I feel a ripple of pride as I pass my Cyclist of the Year trophy that sits with assorted sporting cups on a varnished table at the bend in the corridor. Junior school is in its last throes. At breaktime, I make daisy chains with my best friends Ruth and Jenny in the quadrangle, one of them so long we can thread it wall to wall. We bury it in the maypole hole to keep it fresh.

One afternoon, I surprise myself by stealing away with Emma, the class rebel, on the pretext of taking a message to the headteacher's office. We dawdle back via the music room, with its dented trombones, and then Emma suggests we break into the sports store cupboard. The door handle is made from heavy brass, with a difficult upright button to release the catch. It takes both of us to squash it down. 'Let's jump from up there!' we squeal before climbing a pile of gym equipment. We squelch down onto thick blue crash mats, exhilarated by our wrongdoing. We try out seized-up pogo-sticks, untouched for decades, and nearly break our ankles. We're breathless and hungry for adventure. Emma is more physically developed than me and, in the sweaty haze of our trespass hour, decides to show me the dark hair in her armpits. Then we return breezily to our classroom. Like one of those songs you're obsessed with fleetingly, mine and Emma's friendship lasts for just this day. It's our secret punk song.

There's a strange craze for boob cream among the top-class girls. Kelly says it makes you grow faster. After PE, I hide in my vest, avoiding eye contact while the others pass the tube around. When I force myself to join another new fashion, for *going out* with someone (which seems to involve awkward chats with boys in the playground), I see disappointment in my teacher's eyes. 'I thought you were more mature,' says Mrs Grainger. I shrug but find it wounding. My union with James is over by home time. There is another more pressing matter anyway. In my head, I am running down the wing, skipping around a defender and whipping the ball into the box with the inside of my left boot, probably towards Nigel in his Toon Army socks. There's a soundtrack playing. Keyboards and a drum pad help me cushion the ball as I take it around a tall boy with curly hair. I am heading towards holy places and one of them is Italia '90.

*

Men in navy shorts and white shirts are jogging towards me, red numbers on their backs. Among them, Gary Lineker from my *Shoot!* annual. The singer in sunglasses is telling them to express themselves. They must create space and never give up. A deep, neon bassline drives them – and me, listening – forwards. When something's good, it's never gone. I am still painfully shy. Mum tries to make me brave, offering me 50p to light a match above a bowl of water, but I still can't do it. I only come alive when I'm kicking a ball or listening in my loft room to a song. The team in the music video is the England squad and, as I take in the words, it becomes clear to me that they – we – are going to lift that gleaming gold World Cup.

A ball spins on a finger. It's John Barnes, my favourite Liverpool player, now England's main man. He's a pop star now and doing keepy-uppies in red Adidas behind Bernard Sumner, New Order's frontman and the singer on 'World in Motion'. It's May 1990 and 'Killer' by Adamski – and featuring Seal – has been at number one for a month. Its space-voyage strangeness has opened my mind to a new kind of electronic sound. I'm high on the charts and inhaling the top ten week in, week out: tank fly boss walk jam nitty-gritty and the lyrical Jesse James fill my head while Paula Abdul dances with a cartoon cat. But football and music, together?

Team practice happens after school on Tuesday nights. We chat excitedly about the latest plotline in *Jossy's Giants* as we clatter back up Stockwell Lane in the falling light. Home for tea, I'm muddy and tired but pleased about my inside run from the wing to put Ian through on goal. The boys have years of this ahead. I don't know it, but as the 1989–90 season fades out, I am playing my last-ever matches. On Wednesday lunchtimes, our coach Mr O'Brien – we call him OB – names the line-up for our next fixture. A slow,

The football team 1989/90 season, Castle CE Junior School, Knaresborough. I am second from the left on the second row.

teasing process, each position chalked on the blackboard one by
one, fifteen eager faces watching hopefully. Trepidation becomes
joy when I see the downward stroke of D for Doble in midfield
or on the wing. Away games mean trips in the white minibus to
muddy fields and the muted hostility of our opponents' parents. In
our last home match, I nearly score. I connect, follow through and
the ball pings off the crossbar.

I've been told that football songs are terrible and cheesy (Dad,
again), but this one seems different. This team seem like the Bash
Street Kids from my *Beano* comics: mullets, grins and a Geordie
lad called Gazza. 'We ain't no hooligans,' raps Barnes, 'This ain't
a football song.' The sky is high and the school holidays will soon

stretch out in front of us like a beautiful green lawn. 'World in Motion' gets to number one and stays there for two hot weeks in our final junior school term.

*

I am in two circles of friends. With Ruth and Jenny, I am organising end-of-term lunchtime discos in the school hall. We dim the lights and push back the shiny wooden wall bars to create our dancefloor. Entry is 10p. Groups of friends take turns in overlapping ovals. Somebody cartwheels. Ben moonwalks. The air smells of dust and chewing gum. We three girls learn a routine together, practised in the small hall to Bobby Brown's 'Every Little Step', then performed in the big hall to a real audience. Then I return to the comfort of wall-ball with Kevin, James, Phil and the other boys. We play it with a tennis ball, which is kicked from further out in the yard. Two chalk lines on the bricks mark the goal. The least number of kicks wins. We use culverts to speed our progress and groan when the Victorian drainpipes intervene. The ball is worn and pale brown, like the toes on our shoes.

It's the first day of July when England play their quarter-final against Cameroon. We are several weeks into a sweltering lemonade summer, the back door permanently open. Our cat Alice strolls in and sniffs around, putting her ginger paws up on the table, which also has our feet on it because Mum and Dad are out. Italia '90 mania has taken over our living room: we've plotted England's path to the final in blue biro, and we're drinking in Pavarotti's 'Nessun Dorma', the tournament's signature tune. Tonight's game is taking place in Naples where, the commentators say, the air is humid and heavy. We're worried, in a good way, obeying the tense mood of the nation. The heat, the hype and the hope: it all makes it hard to sit still. Our parents are still out when the match kicks off, and so this new world of football anxiety must be navigated alone. We are seven, eleven and fifteen. We have the TV turned up loud. My big sister Claire is our leader and oversees the situation. England must win to stay in the tournament. England are the favourites to go through. England, Eng-er-land: it's all in our grasp.

David Platt scores on twenty-six minutes and we yelp, sending the cat scuffling to the door. We're still giddy at half time. Love's got the world in motion. Fifteen minutes later, our life of football angst begins when Cameroon are awarded a penalty. We can't look. Cameroon score; of course they do. Oh God. Claire gathers us round and says we must, like the team, regroup. I'm cross because John Barnes, with three lions on his chest, has been substituted. I go for a walk in the garden, see Alice under her favourite bush, and come back slightly calmer.

They'll hit you and hurt you, we had been warned, and within a few disastrous minutes Cameroon score again and I feel sick. Even Kerstin, holding her My Little Pony, has a face of grave concern. The room goes quiet. We clutch things and agree that no one should move. Our actions are clearly influencing the match. I should have never gone to the garden. We hold hands, cross our feet, we pray. Our prayers are answered when Lineker wins a penalty. I can't look but Claire can. She screams. I open my eyes. Goooooaaaaaal! Two-all. We leap into the air, knees tipping the table. We sing for England. And we can hear cheers from the street.

The match goes to extra time and the awful tension returns. Surely, surely. Please, now. I watch through my fingers as Gazza, with his half-mast socks, sends the ball from midfield towards the feet of a darting, eager-eyed Gary Lineker. This is it, this is it. This. Is. It! Arrivederci, it's one on one. And then he's on the floor, the ball rolling tamely away. And then yes! Another penalty. We've got a penalty. Please, we'll never ask for anything else again. Lineker, hair slicked back by sweat, has a serious look in his eye. It's a look we will see again. Oh God. I can't watch. Claire is brave and follows for all of us. Lineker. GOAL. Yesssssss!!! I open my eyes just as Claire grabs me at both my sides. She throws my whole body upwards and I swear my head comes close to the ceiling. I descend back down to the living room, slightly altered forever.

Three days later, on a Wednesday night, Gazza cries, Lineker makes that face again, but this time there is no salvation. England lose to Germany on penalties in the semi-final. It's over. My eyes feel raw, my cheeks ragged. I'm up in my room and vow to avoid 'World in Motion' forever. I must dodge it, banish it. It has broken my heart. We were going to win the World Cup. We were meant to win the World Cup. I know now that music is a volatile substance. My Italia '90 sorrow is deeper because of the song.

3

Sliding the rails

A pale-gold second hand moves to the top of a floating black clock with blue numerals. I savour a few final, unburdened moments. But it is the music that gets me: an urgent orchestra telling me there is no escape now. A map of the world becomes a giant 'SIX' that peels away like a stack of important files. They are the pages of my maths textbook. The theme tune belongs to the *Six O'Clock News* on BBC One and its stern melody orders me to accept my fate. I know I must uncurl myself from the settee and go to my room to start my homework. *Neighbours* is over, Charlene's gone to Brisbane, there's nowhere else to hide. I hear the oven door slam. Mum comes in from the kitchen to find out what's going on with the government. *That woman* is in Brussels again saying things we don't want her to say, apparently. Maggie, not Kylie. I reach for my bag and go upstairs.

School finishes at 3.40 p.m. It takes about fifteen minutes to walk home; over King James Road, past the swimming pool, where fifth-years huddle in smoky alcoves, and from there to the crossroads, where the traffic lights next to the Conservative Club always take forever. I sometimes stand on tiptoes to peep through the tall Georgian window, but all I can see are rows of upside-down spirit bottles along a panelled bar. In my mind, I imagine the chancellor of the exchequer ordering a gin, but I've never actually seen anyone there apart from a woman who once told my mum she would 'vote for a pig so long as it wore a blue rosette'.

I walk home with Lisa. We call in at Woolworths halfway down the high street, mostly to look at the music shelves along the left-hand wall beyond the tills. Maria McKee is at number one with 'Show Me Heaven', the song from the Tom Cruise film *Days of Thunder*. I saw her last week on *Top of the Pops* and, unlike all the others, she sang her song live. Dad says she has a good voice. I'm always pleased when he likes something new. I can hear a trembling passion in the song that, well, leaves me breathless. Whatever the singer is experiencing and wherever she is, it seems like a wonderful place. I feel a twinge of heartbreak for some unknown future, but I manage to shrug it away. Lisa and I go to the shoe aisle that smells of black rubber gym shoes. We breathe in deeply, a weird kind of liquorice thrill. We know this is odd behaviour and we half want the shop staff to notice, but they're all too busy being normal. These are the daydream hours, 4 p.m. until 6 p.m., when our mums don't need to know where we are. In summer, we lie on the grassy banks around the castle, doing stupid voices and hiding from kids in other years. We snigger at the sweat marks on their Global Hypercolor t-shirts. On autumn nights, we hurry back for *Byker Grove*.

These new routines are so different from life in junior school. The town is ours now. We mess about in the market place phone boxes that smell of metal and Saturday night's urine. We go to the top floor of the library and pull out the Hardy Boys' adventures from neat rows of well-thumbed paperbacks, their pages turned at the corners. And we play the 'purse game' – placing our purses on a low wall in Berry's Passage before seeing how far we dare walk before running back, screaming. One day, we make it all the way to Boots before chasing back across the road, hearts beating. In this new world, the call of homework draws stark red lines across the freedom hours, and across our time together. We say goodbye when Lisa turns right at Threshers off-licence, back up the flag-stoned path, a smooth dip in the middle from all the many thousands of feet.

I've been at secondary school for a few weeks, but I'm still not used to the itchy kilt and heavy green tights. Sometimes when I get back home, I get changed into my jeans and play football with Luke from up my street. He supports Wolverhampton Wanderers and, as he dribbles the ball around imaginary defenders, he commentates to his own moves. Steve Bull is always scoring hat-tricks and turning to the crowd for adoration. The ball bangs loudly on the black padlocked gate, but none of our neighbours seem to mind. This is now the full extent of my football world. My studs and shinpads are several weeks retired and lie in the darkness of the understairs cupboard – the 'glory hole' – beyond the toolbox and tins of paint. I've been forced to give up football.

The PE teacher walks towards me in a pink-and-white shell suit, a whistle bobbing around her neck. She's counting us into the hall and ticking us off on a clipboard. 'Ah, you must be Anna,' says Mrs Bolton. 'Are you the one who plays football?' Her question gives me a small moment of hope. 'Yes,' I say, nervously. 'Well, here, you'll do hockey and netball,' she explains.

'And cross-country running.' As I pull on my Hi-Tec trainers, I accept the ruling meekly.

*

On a misty November morning, a new craze. We're sliding down the railings from the canteen block to the lower school playground, next to the tennis courts. The rails are made of grey metal, but painted black. We want to join the club and so we are prepared to risk snagging our tights. We learn fast: it's important to lift your feet clear of the low, red-brick wall beneath that has unseated previous sliders. A muddy embankment with sad shoots of grass meets those who wobble over. As we swoosh together, in races, in pairs, done cautiously with hands at the ready, done with show-off arms outstretched, a tall confident girl from Swaledale called Kim keeps singing *that* song. 'The things you say,' she bellows. 'You're unbelievable!' the group responds. It's the first time I've heard it. We're in a sea of dark-green uniforms, our breath making little clouds in the autumn air. We want to be a part of things and here's where it might start. 'You're *so* unbelievable!' shouts a tall blond boy, Stuart, laughing and turning away.

The school is divided into houses named after the dales of Yorkshire. I am in Airedale. In the real world, it's the urban part of the county that tips into Leeds. In the school world, Airedale is represented by the colour blue and has a reputation for swots. Nidderdale, the red house, is also quite nerdy, but Wharfedale (green) and Swaledale (yellow) are for the sporty and socially powerful. These houses seem to contain people who win things – and who kiss each other. In Airedale, my skills in football and tennis carry little currency. Kim has a crowd of boys around her. She commands them, throws her head back and laughs. One day, she will write me heartfelt letters from a lonely Canada.

When I get home, I hear the song again on the radio. 'Oh!' someone shouts over squelchy keyboards and a cowbell. The guitars are low-slung and non-committal, a musical manifestation of a teenage eye-roll. I am surprised by the singer because he seems young and vulnerable. If I shut my eyes, it might be a song by the school band playing in the main hall at lunchtime, us nodding along but never daring to dance. The singer James Atkin is out of breath, like he's been sliding the rails too. He's also upset with his girlfriend. 'You burden me with your questions,' he laments, 'but don't listen to my replies.' I glimpse the future, but for now I want to understand what he means by purple prose. I listen on repeat while writing English notes with too many adjectives.

'I'm gonna get that one wit plait' is the phrase I hear the next morning as I'm hanging up my Mothercare coat in the first-year cloakroom. I'm feeling self-conscious because I know I'll be dead meat if anyone notices that I'm dressed from a baby shop. I like its green colour and its duffle-style button loops, though, and imagine myself looking poetic. It's too late because the coat and my hairstyle – a long brown plait – have already made me the target of three bullies, all girls. It takes a moment to realise the 'one wit plait' is me. I turn to see the trio – a Yorkshire version of *Heathers*, all hairspray and Fruit of the Loom – standing together in a diagonal formation to block my exit. My heart is beating and my cheeks feel hot. I look at the main bully and ask her to let me pass. 'Nooh, yer can't,' she says, turning to her accomplices for approval.

CONNECTION IS A SONG

I have no plan now and just stand still, hoping for an intervention. In my head I'm singing 'You're unbelievable', extending the last syllable so it sounds like 'unbelieve-baaaawwll'. This time the lyrics are my inner commentary and sung with disgust at their random spite. The interlude, as fractional as the tick of a hand on a floating clock, saves me. For a second, I'm not even there. The bell rings and Miss Baxter, the French teacher, shoos everybody away up the corridor.

*

A song released within the same dewy days as 'Unbelievable' fails to even chart, but will wait for me under mosses in the woods. A Scottish voice babbles from a forest stream, only faintly audible to those who dare to explore. I'm still on the main path, my feet shuffling through fallen branches, brushing past Fanta-orange crunchy leaves, clutching a new pencil case. Elizabeth Fraser and her band, Cocteau Twins, are here and alive in the autumn of my first year at secondary school. Sixth formers with whimsical hair know them, etched into C90 cassette inlays and passed between tender hands. One of them might be my older sister, Claire: a prefect who has the power to throw us out into lunchtime rain but never does.

'Heaven or Las Vegas'. It could be the dreamy soundtrack to a night in a damp glade with a frog, a bat and a kindly witch. There is a chill that itches my soul. A sun that is pronounced 'soon'. This is a different heaven to the one inhabited by Maria McKee. In Fraser's gabbling vocals, I am cushioned by the idea of meadowsweet and starlight, and by the mysteries of the natural world that my mum

28

has taught us to notice. At eleven, I am pressing flowers, drawing dandelions and studying closely the claws on my cat. This song, which exists but I've not yet heard, is already there in the dock leaves and the cuckoo spit.

Next to our house on Ash Mount, above the railway, sits the strange afterlife of a Victorian hospital that later becomes an old people's home. It is condemned and now fills familiar space like a wasteland, its stone walls with ladybirds in the cracks unaware that the bulldozers are coming. For a few months, this gothic playground is ours, with its abandoned Zimmer frames and chairs with the foam falling out. We roam free around the grounds: tennis matches on the fading car-park lines, strange crimes of joint adventure and a sense that we'll soon be arrested – or, later, that we're living inside a Pulp song. With the boys from up the street, we find a way inside via a basement window and take wheelchair races around the abandoned corridors. Doors are left open, and we climb through store cupboards still stocked with starched pillows and grey blankets.

There is a harsh and pleading quality in Fraser's vowels, perhaps even a hint of menace. Rumbling across cattlegrids in the twilight, I am lost in a time I have yet to even find. Music, I realise retrospectively, creates origami folds. We turn together along familiar, sometimes pre-made creases, but we can't imagine the end until it's happened: the you of now confronts the you of a bygone time. The childhood version of you looks in the mirror and sees another with bony shoulders and small breasts. By the time I'm bingeing on the Cocteau Twins – an '80s band and therefore not mine anyway – I'm in my late teens. I call to her, to me, with some words of advice, but the kid on the rails is too fast and has already slipped away on the cold metal.

4

Lessons from Fizz

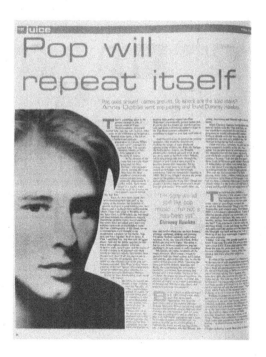

I am not the only one. The sighing afternoons, the painful intimacy of a minor chord, and songs that will carry you through the rest of your life. It seems others have signed up to all this too, and long before me. Others have also written it down. And one of those people is my teacher, Mr Robinson, who shows me that songs become very personal soundtracks.

Robbo, as we call him, and who is really Phil – and Fizz to his brother – has clocked my interest in music through the song 'Torn in Half', a mournful ballad from the soundtrack to the book we are studying, *Buddy's Song*. I'm pretty sure it's not my teacher's sort of thing, but the track is not important; my reaction to it is. A grand, over-sentimental showtune, I am thirteen when it mounts its ambush, its fragile beauty lunging for my heart. The track is hiding on a Chesney Hawkes B-side and tells the tale of fictional teenager Buddy and his sorrow at the divorce of his parents. Back in my listening pose, in the whispery breeze of my loft window, I'm falling into Buddy's world. Hawkes yelps like a wounded animal. I'm look-ing up again, always expecting answers from the sky. The stretched long A in 'laaaasts' ('nothing ever lasts') gives me a strange chill (this is not how we speak in Yorkshire), but I'm comforted when I think of my own parents, two floors below, gently bickering over the washing up.

In school we are reading *Buddy's Song* as a class, paragraph by paragraph, the story circling around our dusty grey portacabin, with its two steps at the entrance covered in gauze to stop us slipping on rainy days. There are two symmetrical classrooms, one on each side, separated by flimsy walls, the desks arranged along the edges so the teacher can pace in the middle and swing around to fire a question at an unsuspecting daydreamer. There's a clock above the whiteboard which is always running slow, and we seem to forever be five minutes from break time. I bring my song to the lesson, feeling nervous about sharing its raw feelings. Mr Robinson pulls out a black cassette deck from the staff cupboard, plugs it in, clicks it open, puts in my tape, and hits 'play'. We sit silently. To my friends, Chesney is the uncool one-hit wonder kid with long blond hair. To me, he is the boy with a voice so beautiful he makes my sides ache.

*

'The One and Only' might be the most over-confident song of the '90s. It is power pop with no subtlety: shiny and plastic like a toy Ferrari. It begins with the sound of something accelerating: a racing track, a runway, a rocket scorching through the clouds. Chesney seems to know a crash landing is likely. It's a Thursday night and I'm watching the video on *Top of the Pops*, and still in my school uniform, when it dawns on me that this song, which could sound arrogant, might be responding to the cruelty of fame, not celebrating it. The lyrics seem to be about trying to keep in touch with your true self. 'I can't wear this uniform without some compromises,' Chesney sings, yearningly. I know the song is from a musical, and that *Smash Hits* wants me to pin Chesney to my wall, but the song's message seems to cut through in a different way to Brother Beyond.

The promo video to 'The One and Only' is set in a cinema that tries to evoke the 1950s. There are back-combed fringes, and popcorn is passed around as two teenage girls settle into their seats. Chesney appears as Buddy, arguing with his on-screen dad, played by Roger Daltrey, an overbearing teddy boy with sideburns. It's then that we see Chesney burst from the screen into three dimensions, the magical moment visible only to us and one of the girls. She is ushered from her seat by a serenading Hawkes, who leads her backstage where he sings to her among theatre props.

Intermittently, our hero is pulled back into the action through the screen, a kind of joust between fantasy and reality. As I watch the story unfold, I realise the girl stepping into fiction is me.

The song swooshes me through the spring of my second year at King James's School. I feel close to every word, every cracking vocal inflection, every sinew of its emotionally exhausting verses. Friendship circles shift and re-order, powerful social hierarchies form. I am on the outside looking in, always with a lyric in my head.[i]

I am finding my feet in school, playing tennis for the girls' team and hanging around the music block. Lisa and I compose a synth tune called 'A Distant Star' on one of the Casio keyboards. It is probably a prog-rock composition, but we don't know, and we have no way of saving it beyond the keyboard's internal memory. It lives for a while on the same machine, in the back of the main practice room, beyond the red metal doors that bang shut. One day, we go again to play it, still pleased with our secret song, and find that it's been erased.

The sound of the *Six O' Clock News* sends me up the stairs. I'm bored of all my pens and I have a dull ache in my left hand from

---

[i] Years later, I interview Chesney in Leeds on the last day of March 2001, which happens to be ten years and a day since 'The One and Only' first reached number one. I mention my childhood love for 'Torn in Half' and he is visibly relieved to find someone who knows any of his other songs. He buys me half a Grolsch. In the ensuing *Leeds Student* article, I describe him as 'older and wiser' (he is twenty-nine). He tells me about the post-fame decade of playing small gigs where my amp 'would blow up in front of five people'. 'I never really did anything wrong,' he explains. 'I was just doing my thing. I was quite a private person, so to be thrust into the limelight was hard, and then for it all to blow up in my face was tough.' He finishes his chat with me wistfully. 'I know I can sing. It's what I've always done.' He has no idea how much I agree.

writing too hard, so I decide to type out my English homework on my parents' new word processor, the Canon StarWriter. There's a thrill in watching the ink cartridge move side to side, spraying little inky jets onto the smooth paper, my words made real. Back in the portacabin, Mr Robinson is asking after my new skills. He wants to know if I'd be interested in helping him create a series of fanzines about his favourite songs. I ask my mum and she says yes. When you try to save anything on the StarWriter, it pauses terrifyingly, makes twitchy grinding noises and bleeps ominously, but it's enough for this new industry: words about music, reading, typing and imagining the places and people in the songs.

I'm just the typist. It's my first-ever job and my wages are paid in two currencies, a cheque for £25 – and the doorway to all his music. The project is called *Let's Make This Precious*, after the Dexys Midnight Runners track, which I've never heard. My task is to turn Robbo's inner musical world, written out in long-hand, into a series of A5 booklets that he will post to his friends with a newly burnished TDK tape. As I tap away at the keyboard, still listening to Chesney, I need to know more about the tracks in these cryptic lists, so I ask him for my own cassette and set about listening to the tracks for myself. As I read through Mr Robinson's elegantly handwritten recollections, trying to keep typing but distracted by the music, I devour stories of youth and hope and disappointment. I learn the secrets of Fizz and Poz, of Phil and Paul, my teacher and his brother, and their boyhood ramblings around rivers, bridges, dreams and plans. It is during these hours in the loft, typing and deleting, re-formatting and praying for the paper tray, that I travel from the bright daylight of Chesney to the dark, brooding small hours with Orbital. It's a *Smash Hits* backflip.

Robbo's tapes take me to a whole new world and so I keep turning them over. Through the hours of feverish typing, I am tumbling through a new and sophisticated universe from Virginia Astley to David Bowie, Kate Bush and This Mortal Coil. There is something else too, in the way that he describes 'sighing out' his last days at university in Canterbury. He writes about 'painfully intimate' lyrics (Gary Numan, 'Complex') and songs to 'carry you through the rest of your life' (David Bowie, 'Heroes'). Through these diaries, I'm peering at someone else's life through music. I'm listening to Echo and the Bunnymen ('A Promise') and reading about Fizz and Poz 'looking out over the cliffs on turquoise days' on the Isle of Wight, 'letting no dark things cloud our vision of life as we knew it should be'. There's always a hint of sadness. Fizz shows me that there's more to loving music than dancing in a garage.

Virginia Astley meets me after school, takes me by the hand and walks me down to the meadow beyond the bend in the Nidd. She makes me aware of the crickets in the long grasses, points out the sand martins on the water and tells me a story about a long-lost soldier returning to his village from war. I am guided towards this magic-real place, in my mind, and on the riverbanks of my hometown, through song. Nature, my place in it, my mum's joyful passion for birdsong . . . it is all stitched together by music. And *this music* — made of church bells, the sound of a breeze on the water, the sepia acceptance of long-ago summers — is a sensation to me. Mr Robinson puts *From Gardens Where We Feel Secure* on his 'instrumentals' compilation and I fall at once under its spell. It sounds like an old but precious paperback book: creamy-white, smelling of rain and with a pressed flower, unseen for a decade, falling from its pages. Astley's mauves, dusty pinks and faded yellows are several dimensions away from the garish pop of the charts. I am in a dream-like state of half-remembered July afternoons. I am a child in search of nostalgia after only thirteen summers.

*

I can hear the old school bell ringing down two flights of stairs. It's teatime: stew with dumplings. I plod down in my green stocking feet, smiling to myself at the music in my head. Claire sits on my left, still in her sixth-form kilt, which is white with red-and-blue tartan stripes, while Kerstin, nine, sits to my right, on the end of the table, her arm stretching towards a glass of orange juice. 'What is he saying?' they ask me, about my teacher's secret diaries. 'He's comparing David Sylvian to a Thomas Hardy poem,' I reply, without looking up, scooping up a potato with my fork.

I'm soon back at my desk beneath the skylight, tapping away on the word processor. Somewhere in the future, I am dancing in the woods, my face turned to the morning sun. Orbital's 'Halcyon and On and On' is almost not real: a looping cosmic playground, a soundtrack from a fantasy world. It feels serious, too, emerging like a castle in purple mist in a medieval dream, its ancient charms smoothed by centuries of briny waves that slap inwards from the sea. Distant female vocals call from dark blue ocean bands, encircling a solitary guitar twang that shifts and glints like sunlight on the water's surface. As the waves recede, I look up from my keyboard and find that I need to blink and run my fingers through my hair.

The song is playing from Mr Robinson's latest tape (the series will ultimately stretch from 1992 to 1997, from songs to instrumentals), with his calligraphy on the label. I am dodging my homework

LET'S MAKE THIS PRECIOUS, VOLUME 7.

with two more songs, and this one is nearly ten minutes long. Halcyon. And on. And on. The real Halcion, which gives the song its name, is an addictive tranquiliser, used to treat insomnia. The Orbital brothers, Paul and Phil Hartnoll, dedicate the track to their mum. Under the window, my toes twitching as I type, I pause to drink in the tune's liquid intensity and find that I am in another galaxy, its layers of stardust building in slow, teasing increments. Two minutes pass before there's even a bassline, and I am light years from the pop world's impatient rush to the chorus. When the bass does eventually arrive, it seems understated and without ego, a gentle alignment of planets, like the best kiss of your life.

There's a fuzzy familiarity in the vocal and it takes my older sister to point out that it's a sample from Opus III's 'It's a Fine Day'. I rewind the tape and re-live all nine-and-a-half minutes – again on and on. In my mind, the ocean waves blend into cities at dusk; the glint of orange sun catches the edge of a skyscraper and becomes the vertical bubbles in a bottle of Lucozade. In turn, this liquid metamorphosis makes me dream of smooth horse chestnuts in the leaves beneath a tree, my hands searching for treasure, my nails muddy. It's only the repeating drumbeat that keeps me anchored to my chair, in the ship that is my room. This is my first voyage into the currents of dance music, so far only glimpsed through Adamski's well-lit portholes. In the future, my friend is giggling, propped up at the base of a tree. It's a few hours after the rave. A group of early-morning joggers run down the forest path, their nylon legs rustling. They stop dead: startled to see us there, lying in the wild garlic.

5

Cassingles

I can *smell* pop music. It's a papery kind of scent, its layers sliding across the things I am chasing: the smooth joy of a pin badge, an eyelinered eye, words about the taste of love. It is in my senses now, in the whiff of strong ink in the cardboard cases of my first cassette singles – a sherbet tang in neon yellow, pink and green – and in the pull-out lyrics and folding inlays with their photos of pop stars holding onto their headphones.

There's a fresh-flavoured optimism wafting over me from the glossy pages of my favourite magazines and, despite my secret passageway to Kate Bush and Brian Eno, I want to be a part of this too: I want the hair-sprayed fringe and the minty teeth. I've never seen *Beverly Hills 90210*, but I convince myself that I can really smell its star, Jason Priestley, his face and neck, via a perfumed strip in *TV Hits*. As I peel back the paper flap, it emits Lynx, the flavour of boys. *Just 17* fills my nose with Impulse and Charlie. I sniff with my friend Lisa who owns the real deal – Impulse (Vanilla Kisses) bought from Superdrug. This is the perfume of our next selves, selves who will go to nightclubs, selves who will know how to kiss.

Our town feels like a seaside town, despite being fifty miles inland. It's the little boats that nudge each other on the riverbank, the hope of an ice-cream day and the chance of the suntrap bench at the bottom of the castle grounds being free on a June afternoon. *Other people* – from Leeds and Bradford and Sheffield – come here to visit the weird side of the river, where Mother Shipton's Cave turns random artefacts into stone. Our town is someone else's day out.

One early morning, I am unexpectedly awake, my eyes open to the dawn with strange ease. I feel light, a floating sensation, but find that I am already alert to the sound of birdsong. Soft air smooths my body like feathers moving from my toes to my face. I can smell the new sun. Pale light streaks through the window's gap, sending particles of dust pirouetting over my duvet knees. I keep still, listening to the distant start of the day: the clang of metal gates in the cattle market beyond the green lamppost, a muffled male voice. But it's the birds that hold me. A blackbird leads the chorus, the others follow in intensely beautiful waves, a heavenly swell of sound; a barely believable orchestral movement, big and overwhelming, and performing to an audience of just me, in bed. A poster rustles free from its Blu Tack. I ignore it, afraid to exit the moment. I feel that I am among the birds. I am inside their world, diving under leaves, jostling for twigs, sensing their fluttering lightness. I think to myself, never wanting it to end, and know quickly that through their song I have just experienced something close to pure happiness.

*

I buy cassettes, three-for-a-pound, from George Heapy's record shop next to the library. My collection so far is an odd mix of pop from several months ago – many are the slightly lesser-loved tracks that followed the hit (Chesney Hawkes, 'I'm a Man Not a Boy'; Chris Isaak, 'Blue Hotel') – and songs by artists that I know my dad likes. Van Morrison's brooding 'Coney Island' (with 'Have I Told You Lately' on the B-side) nestles in my musical shoebox alongside Take That's 'Promises', which comes with a free stencil, TT inside a circle. I tattoo my schoolbooks, risking mockery as well as devaluing what will one day become a sought-after piece of pop merchandise. For now, I'm more interested in the little shapes that I make everywhere in blue pen. Pop music smells like the varnished benches at the back of Mr Edwards' science lab and the wet Berol ink of lyrics scrawled in the back of a book.

The bargain bin is a wicker basket positioned beneath Heapy's main shop counter. Rummaging through it demands a certain confidence, a public display. Crouching down puts you in the way of others approaching the till, but standing up risks catching the eye of Julia, the woman in charge of the shop and daughter of the owner. Mr Heapy himself sits on a large wooden chair – my dad calls it Heapy's throne – in the back room, surveying his market town CD kingdom. I don't expect they are marketing their stock at girls with their pocket money, so I keep a low profile, occasionally plucking up the courage to ask after a poster.

Down here on the floor, I'm looking for a tape to make up today's trio, while sniffing the odour of old carpet underlay, dark-green and rubbery. I catch something else in the air each time the door clatters open and I realise it's mouse droppings, mingling with Harry Connick Jr and his cover of Frank Sinatra's 'It Had to Be You', in heavy-duty, expensive-smelling cardboard. I choose Tears For Fears' 'Sowing the Seeds of Love', which has a sweeter fragrance, perhaps influenced by the sunflowers on the cover.

With my three new–old tapes, I cross the cobbles to Maynews and find the latest edition of *TV Hits* with Phillip Schofield on the cover and a giant pull-out poster of Marky Mark Wahlberg inside. What I really want is the 1992 wallchart on the other side: I'm excited to see the year ahead mapped in yellow boxes. I wonder what will happen in each of those weeks. The poster smells of discos and fizzy drinks, and as I pin it up, I'm tempted to chew the Blu Tack like gum. When my sister interrupts with her Kylie tape, I'm enjoying the gluey scent of a freshly peeled sticker and the anticipation of where to stick it – school folders for all-day eye candy or the side of the wardrobe, where Liverpool used to be – for a sense of permanence. I balance cassette inlays on my nose as I listen on my bed, inhaling the concertina folds with their lists of studios, producers and musicians. A hierarchy of pop. A pop workforce. 'A. Linn', Dad informs me, is a machine and not a man.

CASSINGLES

At school, I have been called up to play for the under-14s tennis team. I'm paired with Kim, the 'Unbelievable' girl, who hits the ball hard from the baseline while I scurry around the net with my battered red Browning racquet, called the Invador Jr, which is scratched around the rim from playing in the car park. It has a stag's head on the strings, which I reblacken from time to time with a marker pen. Kim and I hit well together and even though she still scares me, we make a good duo, chuckling at the girls from the private school with their giant sports bags and elbow supports. They can't seem to take a point off us and we win with ease. It's not quite the same as being in the football team, but it's close, and I get my mum to sew the yellow stripes of victory onto my gym skirt.

In form time on a Tuesday morning, a boy called Lee pulls out a sticky, half-eaten lump of nougat, the type you buy in Woolworths, half pink and half white, sugary and chewy. I make the mistake of calling his contraband goods 'noo-gah' and before I know it, the whole class has turned on me to mock my 'posh' pronunciation. 'It's nugget! *Nug-get!*' they claim. In defiance, I call for our tutor, Mr Keogh, also a French teacher, to settle the argument. I'm so sure I will be vindicated that I feel warm and proud inside, brimming with delight at the ignorance about to rain down on my peers. Then Mr Keogh leans over the desk and says, 'Technically, Anna, you're right. But where I'm from we also say *nugget* . . .' I'm crushed and hurry home to listen to my tapes.

*

There's talk of Take That, the boy band from across the Pennines in Manchester, playing in our neighbouring town, Harrogate. It's

45

CONNECTION IS A SONG

a weird kind of rumour that seems to have no substance and is coupled with the claim that Mark Owen, the cute one, has a wooden leg. It's all nonsense and I feel defensive of the band whose cassingle I've had for weeks, with 'Do What U Like' on the B-side, the video for which features the boys flailing around in jelly and ice cream, dolloped across their smooth chests and spattering from their leather tassels. Mum turns a blind eye.

Once You've Tasted Love is the song that should make Take That everybody's new favourite band. But I find the single in the basket of rejects just a fortnight after its release, a dismal failure, its highest chart position is number forty-seven. Nobody gets it, but I can't believe my luck and lovingly add it to my shoebox. The song starts with a bleeping sound from the depths of a dancefloor that I still can't reach. I look disastrously young (because I am so young) and this will go on for a while. There's a soulful female vocal and a rapid, shuffling drumbeat, both calling me to a sweaty podium where Gary, Robbie, Jason, Howard and Mark might be performing, their muscles glossy under spotlights. As I listen on my bed, I can smell the dry ice; my lips taste strawberry lip gloss-sweet. I want to be in a faraway club, in dark but glittered corners.

I know it's the good boy Gary Barlow singing the lead vocal, but his voice sounds different – gravelly – as he beckons me to another world. The chorus gives me a half-pipe swoosh into a giant party hangar. I desperately do not want to be a school girl with a ponytail. Gary sings about the taste of love, tells me that it's 'just the beginning'. He knows my head is spinning.

*

CASSINGLES

While Take That are still struggling to invade the charts, a song with a split personality burns into my tender heart. I don't know that I am loving a track about a moon landing hampered by beautiful women with evil intent, but that is the strange sci-fi inspiration (a 1950s film titled *Cat Women of the Moon*) for 'Stay' by Shakespears Sister. The band name is also a song by the Smiths, albeit spelt differently, and this will eventually connect my late teens with this time. For now, that's in the future, much like the storyline to this weird, witchy song.

It is *Top of the Pops* night, and we are watching the video for the UK's brand-new number one. We see singer Marcella Detroit on a spaceship as she tends to the sorrows of a man on his deathbed. Siobhan Fahey (a post-Bananarama reincarnation) arrives as the Angel of Death and the pair tussle over the poor man's fading soul. It's a demonic joust in thick eyeliner and black leather, Detroit's sweetly sung lyrics about the 'darkness of your dreams' broken into by Fahey's deeper-voiced chant from somewhere in the restless after-life. *You better hope and pray.* She smirks, twitches and grins at this scene of imminent grief, her black sequins twinkling as she licks her lips.

The song, the story and its delivery beguile us three sisters as we sit, staring at the TV on a Thursday evening. It's a gothic pantomime and – just like the real panto[i] we have just been to in Harrogate – we are willing on the dark arts. Fahey, who later tells

---

[i] At *Dick Whittington* in Harrogate Theatre in January, we invent a terrible game with the unwanted toffees from our post-Christmas tin of Quality Street. We unwrap the sweets, take a toothy bite – enough to be very visible, not enough to change the sweet's overall shape – and then rewrap each one carefully. Whenever the actors throw chocolates into the audience from the stage, which is often, we add our damaged goods into the hail of silver and gold from our seats on the balcony. This hilarious act heightens our panto experience as we gaze into the darkness in hope of glimpsing a horrified recipient. Mum has no clue about our unpleasant little distraction.

Melody Maker that she was playing 'a camp, drunken, guzzling sort of . . . thing', inspires me to smear on darkest black Rimmel eyeliner and scowl into the bathroom mirror.

The track stays at number one, stalking the nation with its cartoon wickedness, from February all the way to the middle of April and the chance of a new UK government. We sisters play our strangest game – the fake pollsters – in the run-up to the vote, but only when Mum and Dad are out. It's a phone prank, but unlike other kids who do silly voices and slam the phone down, we dial random numbers on the green landline in the corner of the living room and say, in our young voices: 'We are calling from Ipsos MORI to ask you how you intend to vote on Thursday.' A surprisingly high number of people respond to our enquiries and so we keep a tally and inform Mum that the Tories are going to win, at least in Harrogate and Knaresborough. We only ever blow our cover when respondents say they plan to vote for the Liberal Democrats, shouting 'Paddy Pants-down!' (a tabloid nickname for the party's leader, Paddy Ashdown), before cutting off the call in breathless giggles.

'Stay' is still top of the charts when Mum is berating the *Sun* on election day in Spar. She points out the row of newspapers to me, piled along the left-hand side of the shop as we come in through the door where the wire shopping baskets are stacked. 'What a stupid headline,' she says, gesturing to the image of Neil Kinnock, the Labour leader, with his head inside a lightbulb. The caption reads: 'If Kinnock wins today will the last person to leave Britain please turn out the lights.' I don't truly understand it, but something tells me he won't win. 'If this world is wearing thin, and you're thinking of escape,' sing Shakespears Sister, as I sink back onto my bed and look at the night sky, hoping to see a shooting star, like the one in the music video. We wake up to Kinnock's defeat. By Sunday, Right Said Fred are at number one with a song called 'Deeply Dippy'.

6

Lisa's bedroom

In Lisa's hallway ready for a night out fuelled by fizzy wine from Spar.
My fake fur coat is borrowed from Claire. (Photo taken by Lisa's mum,
Lynn Ibbotson)

CONNECTION IS A SONG

It's early evening on a school night. I'm up in Lisa's room on Whincup Avenue. We come here after lessons to listen to seven-inch singles and tapes. We're not obvious soulmates, Lisa and me, but our houses are both in the town centre, which binds us by geography. I'm into sport and doing my homework. Lisa's into make-up and magazines. We both love talking about pop music. Everyone else seems to live on estates in the identikit outskirts, so the market place and high street are ours. We combine this territorial advantage with humour. We make each other laugh with misheard lyrics, imaginary characters, accents and impressions of our teachers.

Sometimes I go home first to get changed, returning the short way by climbing up the rusty, slightly bending green lamppost on my street, a ponytailed cat burglar, hoisting myself over the wall and scampering across the cattle market through pens that smell of straw and pig muck. This saves me a five-minute walk and gets me back to Lisa's with more time to talk about the boys that she fancies.

Tonight, we're still in our uniform: green V-neck jumpers and kilts, which we've rolled up at the waist to make shorter. Our shoes are lined up neatly downstairs because Lisa's mum runs a very tidy home, with well-Hoovered stairs and porcelain ornaments. She's very strict about this sort of thing. I have fake Doc Martens. Lisa has loafers with a low heel. No footwear is permitted on the greyish pink carpet that we brush back and forwards idly with our stocking feet.

The house smells of cigarettes and air freshener. There is a Yellow Pages in the hall, but hardly any books. The alcoves and shelves sit well-dusted but empty. Lisa's parents are kind to me;

her dad is a football fan who invites me into the living room to experience the euphoria when Leeds United become First Division champions in 1992. The kitchen always feels humid with things on the hob: boiling vegetables and gravy. Lisa's mum sends me home when the tea is ready, perhaps knowing that my mum will be wondering where I am.

Back upstairs, I sit sideways on the windowsill with Lisa, our toes on her bedspread with its pink and white flowers. The room has the aroma of feet and Impulse deodorant. There are Care Bear stickers on the upright mirror, some half torn away. Lisa leafs through her new copy of *More!* magazine and we spend a while looking at the sexual position of the fortnight, turning the page sideways in case that gives us a better view. When we're not prodding at our future selves, we record silly voices on Lisa's tape deck. Two of our characters are the 'disco grannies', old women who rant at the world but lighten up when a favourite tune comes on, often Justin Hayward with Mike Batt and the London Philharmonic Orchestra doing 'The Tracks of My Tears', one of Lisa's mum's records. We've also created – and neither of us really know why – a fantasy figure called Elder Devil, the most powerful of dark forces, who administers imaginary punishments to both of us, and to people we know. Annoying teachers and mean boys incur his wrath. Craig, who called me flat-chested in double science, is several times cursed.

Lisa's music collection is a funny mix of seven-inch records from the '80s, a few Motown singles, most of Kylie Minogue's hits and some showtune hand-me-downs. But tonight, we're listening to a ninety-minute tape on a black mini-system tucked in beside the wardrobe. On it, East 17's 'Deep', which Lisa has painstakingly recorded from the radio again and again, nine times on each side, a continuous loop only interrupted by fragments of DJs and the abruptly cut-off opening notes of other songs. It's been a project, this, and now Lisa is basking in the certainty of hearing her favourite song on repeat without having to jump back down to rewind the tape.

The best chats happen like this when we are listening to music and looking outwards together across her neighbours' gardens, criss-crossed with washing lines. There's a half-inflated football by a plant pot in the foreground that belongs to Lisa's brother. Our eyes cast further, beyond a row of garages to the bowling green. Lisa is telling me about a squaddie who is stationed in our neighbouring town that she's been kissing. I ask her if he's good, with absolutely no idea of what I want or expect her to say. She doesn't say anyway, but she smiles to herself and avoids meeting my eyes.

'Deep' is wafting into the air through the open window. We don't know if the bowlers can hear our chatter, or the song, as it fills the darkening sky. The bowlers are old people we probably know, dressed all in white. They move slowly and never seem to look up. But it's to their neat square of gentle activity that we always gaze. Tonight, we share one cigarette, carefully dabbing the ash onto the outer part of the window ledge where it won't be seen by Lisa's mum. We can see the glow of somebody else's cigarettes in the gloom and hear scraps of conversation. We think it's boys we might know from the Stockwell estate, so we turn up the volume. We have our own bad boys, on a loop.

The operatic sample at the start of 'Deep' rolls around again, floating over a hip-hop beat that seems to mimic the low, confident positioning of East 17's voluminous combat trousers. These are council-estate lads, but southern ones and cute ones, rappers as well as singers. Their logo is a graffiti-tagged cartoon dog, and their natural habitat is the pool room where things might kick off. They are the kind of boys our mums would hate us to like. But they are all over *Smash Hits*, *Top of the Pops* and breakfast TV, these lads who show us their pants.

Sitting in the window, listening to the track for the ninth time, it finally hits me that the song is all about sex. I now realise that it might be the dirtiest song I've ever heard, but somehow I have not noticed until now, and nor, it seems, has anyone else. 'Deep' is all over the mainstream, on Radio 1 and our local station, Stray FM. But Tony Mortimer, the lyric writer and singer, doesn't want deep conversation, as I had previously thought. He's feeling and fumbling, and he wants to do it until his belly rumbles. Not just that, but he's going to 'lick you where you love him to go'. 'In I go, oh, deep and down deeper . . . like an ocean.' He turns the lights down low, but it's too late to save me, sitting next to my friend in my school uniform, failing to contain the red heat of severe embarrassment rising through my cheeks.

It's with Lisa that I first get drunk, down by the river. Procuring alcohol is not an easy process in a small town where everyone knows your mum. I look so young. Neither of us dare to raid our parents' cupboards, so it's down to Lisa, in her leather jacket and plucked eyebrows, to walk into our chosen shop and ask coolly for a bottle of strawberry-flavoured 20/20. I wait around the corner in Finkle Street, nervous, because Lisa is taking a while. But there she is strolling towards me with an undaunted tread. Not too bouncy, not too swift, the pink bottle tucked neatly under her arm. I join her from the shadows, also trying to be breezy, and we head to Waterside.

CONNECTION IS A SONG

We take little sips under moonlight as the boats make ghostly clunking noises. After an hour of this, with Lisa still humming East 17, we test ourselves trying to walk straight along the white parking lines because we've heard that's how you diagnose drunkenness. We wobble and giggle, declaring ourselves shit-faced. We are not, but we decide to hide behind a car when Ruth's mum drives by anyway.

I am still waiting for my first kiss. Who we might kiss next – or kiss at all – is the main talking point. But between that, and the silly voices, something is changing. We've grown up together and moved up from the local junior school to the same form in high school. The age of clubbing and drinking and boys is in view, but Lisa wears lacy tops and pearlescent lip balm, and I begin to feel that I'm holding her back.

*

Nanny Connie was a garden-whisperer, forever showing us buds and shoots poking from terracotta pots despite the frost and snails. Her sunflowers grew cartoonishly large and gathered their own kind of local fame. The house had a window at ground level that allowed us sisters to swing through, like a porthole, into the room where we set up our fake supermarket. A former primary school teacher, Nanny loved us in very practical ways. She spent hours giving us 'problems' – little quiz questions pitched perfectly at our different ages. 'If apples are five pence, how many can I buy with 20p?' 'If I have twelve slices of bread, how many sandwiches can I make?' Nanny let us play shop – weighing her lentils, sugar and flour – for hours on end, pretending that we were running a busy grocery store while messing up her kitchen.

LISA'S BEDROOM

She saw me clearly and fed me a steady diet of old football magazines that would appear weekly on the rattan chair by the front door, with Grandad's well-polished shoes pushed beneath. The hall smelled of umbrellas. A friend whose son had grown up donated the stash that Nanny then gave me in thrilling consignments of twos and threes. They were vintage 1980s editions in perfect condition, so I immersed myself in the cup finals and transfer deals of an already bygone era; someone else's nostalgia.

It is with Lisa that I will later turn Nanny Connie's empty cottage into Teen Party HQ and the theme will be the 1980s, an innovation in the mid-1990s. Madge Bishop from *Neighbours* will greet people on the underside of the toilet lid in my granny's bathroom with its carefully nurtured plants still pressing their gnarly stems against the window. A-ha and Wham! will invade the greys and blues of Grandad's landscape paintings in the low-beamed living room. A boy from Boroughbridge will smoke on the stairs and open the door to Grandad's old room without asking. When teen fumblings happen in this place, a set of rosary beads left there by my uncle will clink from the handle of the second drawer down.

The party will take place during a long sweep to summer, a few years after the 'Deep' meditation and on a night where Nanny's tidy house becomes a mess of Adidas stripes and Gallagher-ish haircuts. I will walk through the familiar rose-framed door and find a cloud of Lynx where the inky smell of my football comics used to be, the tang of chewing gum instead of Grandad's oil paints. I will look down at cider-spattered boot-cut jeans and listen to the clink of Hooch bottles. Light-filled evenings might try to chat us up through the long grass in the paddock where there was once a lonely horse. And Lisa will disappear with the boy from Boroughbridge. After looking for her, I will instead go outside and ask the smokers not to put their cigarette butts in Nanny's geraniums.

7

A funny feeling

Summer is about to unfurl its first buds. The air feels light and warm, so we leave our coats at home. It's the middle of May 1993, the day my older sister and I will find a pop music portal in the back of Asda. We're on our fortnightly trip to the supermarket in Harrogate, the next town along from ours. We go with our mum to help her carry the shopping, each of us older sisters handed two carrier bags to heave onto the Asda bus. It always seems to tip us forwards, this stubby little vehicle. We lurch, unbalanced by potatoes, our hands grooved by harsh plastic handles. We don't want to be seen; we are embarrassed not to have a car for this sort of mission. But these trips have their extra rituals, and today is a day that we will talk about in thirty years' time.

As our mum circulates with her trolley, our younger sister Kerstin riding on the wheels, Claire and I go to the music department. There's no one much around, so we try out all the buttons on the hi-fi systems: graphic equalisers, super woofers, bass boosters. Black plastic towers of our dreams: CD, FM radio and cassette; Sony, Kenwood, JVC. We want them but we can't have them, so we retune them all to Radio 1.

We head for a sacred space – the top forty wall with its new releases propped in angled grooves, the smell of cardboard and little plastic fronds that scatter from the middle of a CD like stamen. Pop's new blooms. Ace of Base top the chart with 'All That She Wants'. There are gaps outside the top ten, but the number one shelf is well stocked. Ace. Of. Base. In big red letters. The song comes in four versions: the one we all know from the radio, a 12-inch extended play, a bhangra edit and a 'madness' mix, which is frantic like a fairground ride, a sped-up mess of hi-hats and squelchy saxophones. I like it, but I can't afford to buy it. Our eyes scan for other treasure, but I am distracted by the televisions hanging above our heads and all playing the same concert.

I gaze upwards, entranced, my eyes darting from screen to screen. A rumble of bass. There's a familiar high-pitched synth – in minor key, a steady note – that's finding me like a searchlight. A shudder travels down my spine. There's a rush in my head too, but it comes with a strange feeling. A dark, excited, slightly guilty feeling. Sassy finger clicks beckon. I am staring at legs and torsos moving in sync, black sequins, greased muscles; a wiry, powerful body, and the song – which I already know, but *not like this* – is bouncing at me with metallic ruthlessness from Asda's neon rafters. I glance around, feeling watched. Claire is looking through a bargain bin of tapes and hasn't yet noticed the state that I am in.

*

Three years earlier, the spring of 1990, I'm hiding inside a football comic as the moons of 'Vogue' orbit school life. Everybody in my class is trying out voguing. Madonna's new song is at number one. A hymn to the freedom of dancing, stolen from the subterranean Latino clubs of New York City, we have no idea what we are doing. We are kids in the top class of primary school attempting to do the moves. Neil is in his *Teenage Mutant Hero Turtles* jumper. I'm trying it in my grey school cardigan. We strike a pose in the playground, right-angled arms first, then with a spiralling motion, we flail our hands around our heads. Our lips are pursed and we freeze-frame our bodies between each shape imagining we're in the music video.

There's a status to knowing the lyrics, especially Madonna's coolly delivered spoken-word segment (we're not sure if it's a rap), which we recite but don't understand. Greta Garbo, and Monroe, Dietrich and DiMaggio. They might be the lost Mutant Turtles. The names feel good in our mouths. Ruth, who is sophisticated and has her own make-up, reckons there is a double meaning to the bit about Rita Hayworth giving good face.

I do not try to work it out. The song is all around us, it's the sound of now. Madonna does the pose in every magazine, we see her weekly on *Top of the Pops*, and we watch again on the *Chart Show*; those piercing eyes, her dark lips parted, the gap between her front teeth, and her bouncing blonde curls framed by vogueing hands. Her image, this Hollywood movie-pop-star superbeing, in black and white, is everywhere, and on a small round badge, free with *Smash Hits*, that I keep hold of but don't yet wear.

*

Back in Asda, Claire is rooting through the discounted cassettes. I am still standing, staring, an alien sensation filling me. I look down at myself to check I'm still me. I'm in the clothes my mum has put me in. Green corduroy trousers. Hi-Tec trainers with a plastic logo. Madonna is in a pointy bra and tight black shorts with a chunky leather belt, her hair in blonde ringlets. She's performing to a massive crowd that moves like a murmuration of starlings, somewhere far away. The venue is huge and echoey. The cameras cut to close-up adoring faces as she arches her back like a cat. Madonna, the dominatrix, with her army of dancers, is pushing her body towards them and towards me. Asda's checkouts blip bleep in the background. I look around again and Claire is there, with a tape in her hand. She looks at me and then looks at what I'm looking at, with a blank expression. There's a pause. 'She gives me a funny feeling,' I eventually tell my sister, my voice more wistful than I expect, but these are the first words I find to explain myself.

Claire has found a Saint Etienne single that she read about just the other day – 'Five best sounds of the moment' – in the *Independent on Sunday*. Mum and Dad's newspaper has given Claire, and me, an important lead. A clue, a sniff of fandom, a disco beam into our new pop life. The cover is Battenberg-mysterious in pop-art stripes of pink and orange. 'S.a.i.n.t' spells itself in diagonal white letters. You may be in Asda, the tape says to us, but this is not Bon Jovi. Step this way, we'll meet you on the other side, next to the café with the Pepsi sign.

*

Sarah Cracknell is dancing, superimposed over a cityscape. It's probably London. Claire and I often dream of London and its strange place names. Portobello. Angel. Elephant. We imagine mugs of tea on plastic tablecloths in cafes with Italian names. In our minds, it's always spring there.

We're watching the *Chart Show* again on a Saturday morning. A heart-shaped buckle gleams from Sarah's belt. She's wearing a black choker around her neck. On her t-shirt, it says 'Hysteric Glamour', a fashion brand from Japan, says Claire, who reads *Elle* magazine and knows these things. Sarah is dancing in that floaty pop star way, but there's something self-conscious about her too. She doesn't terrify me like Madonna. Sarah is the singer in Claire's new favourite band. Pete Wiggs, the keyboard player, is wearing a plastic golden crown that looks like it came from a children's dressing-up box. A pretend king. Debsey, the other singer, shimmers in pink and white stripes. We want to dance like Debsey, with her Northern Soul shuffle and eyeliner.

Fluty synths flutter skywards. The video cuts away to Pete and Sarah sitting in a windswept Trafalgar Square. Pete, the fake monarch, is in cheap ermine. Sarah is the heartbroken girl of the lyrics. Someone's done her wrong. It's not fair, they don't care. Eventually we see Bob, the other boy in the band, gazing intensely into the camera lens. These are people we'd like to meet. They seem to be pop stars playing at being pop stars.

*

Claire's treasure turns out to be a beautifully sad ballad called 'Hobart Paving', released as a double A-side alongside 'Who Do You Think You Are', a cover of a '70s track by a band called Candlewick Green. Saint Etienne's is a disco-pop reworking, glittery but, like its sister track, mournful, a soundtrack to a film. Claire is a nearly grown-up, has her own money and buys the tape. Soon we are reunited with our mum and little sister. They know nothing of our dual pop epiphanies. I don't know either, but I know that being a music fan is about much more than listening to songs. It's about powerful feelings, adventure and exploration. A flirt with the unknown, it makes you secretive. I am falling in love with the idea – and danger – of Madonna, but I'm also visiting London's parks and the dreams of another time and place with Saint Etienne.

A FUNNY FEELING

After helping Mum unpack the shopping, Claire plays her new cassette to death. We peep out through the windows to see trains emerge from the dark mouth of the railway tunnel under the high street, streaks of light shooting by: people, going to cities. Outside my window, leaves from the sprawling Virginia creeper rustle in the night air. It is home to several birds' nests. My room is directly above Claire's room. When she hits play on her ghetto blaster, her soundtrack is my soundtrack too.

I have my own cassette deck, but I find myself listening through the floor instead as I lie on my bed, looking through the diagonal window up to the sky. Muffled, bass-heavy versions of Claire's songs wire themselves to my brain. 'Starfish and coffee, maple syrup and jam . . .' sings Prince. 'Butterscotch clouds, a tangerine, and a side order of ham,' I reply. Claire also listens to All About Eve, a folk-rock band whose singer's voice weaves up through the leaves on the side of the house. Claire spends hours by the window, making the same eyes with purple eyeshadow and powder, her face pale, surrounded by dark bangs of hair. But there's something more direct about this other sound.

With each play of Claire's new band – *our* new band, with the name of a French football team, St Etienne – the rising, twinkly notes of 'Who Do You Think You Are' pierce the floorboards and shimmer through the carpet, into my mattress, up into my body, to my cheeks and into my ears. It's there when I'm doing my homework, and again when I'm laying out my uniform on the banister, ready for the morning. I hear it as I pack my bag: heavy, plastic-covered textbooks for science and maths, soft pencils for art, a slim homework diary that my mum needs to sign, my pencil case and my calculator with its Tipp-Exed label. I don't mind the song on repeat. In fact, I want it on repeat. I want to stay in the world of the song. 'Who am I? I'm just a girl, who only wants to try to do what's right.'

*

I dare to return to Madonna. I can't shake the uneasy Asda feeling and so I find a way to acquire her albums cheaply from the underground market in Harrogate. There's a music stall at one end, with CDs and cassettes, with the feel of a forlorn tape carousel in a motorway service station. The cassettes are locked away in plastic columns that squeak as they spin. One of them lurches in and out of elliptical orbit as a man with a carrier bag swivels in search of Genesis. I save up to buy two Madonna albums at a time. But it's awkward because only the shopkeeper, an older man with a permanently puzzled face, can unlock my choices. 'At the top, the one where she's in her bra,' I mumble, my face feeling hot, crushed by the sound of my own voice, and pointing at *Like a Virgin*, hoping no one from school walks by. He wraps it in a brown paper bag, like market fruit, and hands me my change.

Saint Etienne are still very much my sister's new thing and, unlike Madonna in her far-off mega dome, they bring with them a Monopoly board of reachable places and possibilities: London maps, cafés with squeezy bottles, a glimpse of the beehived '60s viewed through the Technics decks of a rave. It's through them that connections to other bands begin to unfurl – Denim, Kenickie, Pulp and Blur. Bands who sing about cups of tea and odd but harmless characters that we recognise from our town. This is a world we might already know. But Claire is four years older and leaving me behind.

A FUNNY FEELING

The Madonna feeling hovers at the back of my mind. Is it a crush? Am I scared? I think it's partly a terror that someone so sexual and confident can exist. I am afraid but I know I must follow the feeling to see what happens next. I see Madonna performing again when I'm round at Jenny's house. I've cycled over, past the swimming pool and the school, confused by houses that all look the same, but relieved when I spy the crescent and her mum's red Astra parked just beyond the tree on the front lawn where we climb and sit in summer. Jenny's parents have satellite TV, an exotic thrill, and we binge watch the music channels while eating microwave chips in little boxes.

An old MTV Awards performance is on. This time Madonna is bewigged and powdered, swirling through a faux-Viennese ball. She sashays between dancers in silk pantaloons, a powerful grande dame in a bustle, wielding an ornate paper fan in perfect sync. It is 'Vogue', of course. Madonna is completely, terrifyingly, in control. She's like no one else on Earth that I have seen, and she is telling me the dancefloor is my escape route.

Secret track 1

Pop junk

A scrawled felt-tip pen means nothing to you but everything to me. 'Anna rhymes with . . .?' writes Sarah Cracknell on my 12-inch copy of 'Avenue', which I have taken with me to an interview with Saint Etienne for Leeds Student *at Leeds Metropolitan University. The joke is because I have just asked Sarah and Pete to explain the identity of the mysterious Maurice. 'And then I shall go back to Maurice,' whispers Sarah in the song's cirrocumulus end sequence with its harpsichords and clowns. I never do get a full answer –*

'just someone we knew' — but the record, with its cryptic tattoo, travels with me from that day onwards.

A couple of hours later, 'This one's for Anna!' are the most surprising words that I have ever heard at a gig. The crowd is dappled in green and red light, Sarah is in sequins, and in my pocket the Dictaphone tape with the recording of my interview. She dedicates 'Nothing Can Stop Us' to me — a beautiful surprise — but I am mid-kiss with a boy called Joe and therefore nearly miss it. The tape in my pocket is a time capsule.

Another night in Leeds. Emmy-Kate Montrose's yellow plectrum sails through the air, almost in slow motion, bur very definitely towards my outstretched hand. The Kenickie bassist has just finished the final song, 'In Your Car', and flings the tiny piece of plastic as she puts down her instrument and exits the stage. My sister Claire is standing disbelieving at my side and, for a nanosecond, moves to grab it from me. She calls me lucky and does so often. I go home and add my acquisition to a shoebox full of gig tickets and Nicky Wire's feathers: my very first relics of fandom, from the Manic Street Preachers' Doncaster gig in 1996. I never will be truly sure how they ended up on me.

8

NME territory

Under my feet, the grass is pale yellow, its straw-like spikes smoothed by the weight of many thousands of Adidas Gazelles. I am in my Blur fairytale castle t-shirt from *The Great Escape* tour and staring towards the stage, which looks like a giant ghetto blaster in the evening sun. I've spent my £15 budget on noodles, a pint of lager and the official programme, which I'm trying to keep flat by wedging under my belt at the back of my jeans. I'm about to watch Oasis play Knebworth.

Back at our house, a little while before this trip to enemy turf, Saint Etienne's 'So Tough' is wafting through the middle floor, up the loft stairs and through the heavy wooden door with its ironic Teletubbies 'Anna' name tag (it is still there thirty years later, a relic of a bygone family joke). Since the Asda epiphany, Claire and I have been creating our own pop world. We tape songs from Radio 1 – Mark and Lard, John Peel – and we craft cassette covers using Letraset and abstract pictures from magazines, choosing images we think fit our new music mood: pylons at sunset, a scrap of '70s wallpaper, an advert for ketchup. I've fallen in love with Blur, a band who name their gigs after sugary tea and whose songs invoke TV sitcoms about eccentric English characters, many of whom I recognise from my hometown. Colin Zeal, an affable man with a plausible plan, is my friend's dad who sometimes gets the train. Mr Robinson, with his respiratory problems and a mason's ring, is not the same man as my teacher, but I've seen him in the fishing tackle shop.

On Saturdays, we sit on the living room floor, poised at the video player to record the indie top ten onto our shared VHS, known as the 'kids' tape'. It is labelled in marker pen to stop Dad taping over our pop treasures with the *Coronation Street* omnibus. We wait, hoping that *our* songs – Suede, Stereolab, Saint Etienne, Longpigs, Marion – will feature, and pray that they won't be fast-forwarded after the first chorus. I secretly love 'Crazy for You' by boyband Let Loose, but I keep this from my sister, listening to it on my own while staring at Boris Becker's beautiful blond eyelashes in a picture pinned up by my bed. It's the tear-inducing tumbling pianos that go so well with his freckles.

We hunt for Fred Perrys in Oxfam and I find a perfectly preserved '80s mod-era shirt for £1.20: a joyous day. Claire buys *Melody Maker*, I buy the *NME*, and then we swap. I'm learning guitar chords through sore fingertips. 'There She Goes' by The La's (G–D–C–D) is my first proper indie song, allowing me to retire 'Puff the Magic Dragon'. We sisters are about to choose which teams to support, which bands to make ours. I have bagsied Blur; Claire will take Pulp. Kerstin, who is young and will need to play catch-up, opts for the Charlatans. Oasis don't make our shortlist. When I first see Liam and Noel on TV, I earnestly believe they are a Beatles tribute act.

Everywhere we are being asked to take sides, and not just through our private sibling rivalries. British or American, north or south, Damon or Brett. Out in the world, on the streets, we *want* to be outsiders, but we want to be the ones with inside knowledge, a copy of *London Fields* by Martin Amis, and zip-up tops from long-defunct German football teams, found in vintage shops in Leeds. We read about the so-called British music takeover in *Select* magazine, which Claire buys, and we're guiltily glad to see hairy American boys being set upon by bands who sing about net curtains. We believe there is another tribe for us, away from the lads on the high street in white shirts and Reebok Classics who puke on Fridays outside the pizza shop.

CONNECTION IS A SONG

I look in the mirror and see a girl with a ponytail and a halo of curls. My teeth are crooked. I don't see the person I can feel myself becoming. I still look too young to get into pubs and the constant fear of being turned away, causing my friends to be denied entry too, keeps me in my bedroom, playing music, looking at the sky. When I can finally get away with ordering my own Pernod and lemonade, I develop a strong desire to smash the pub jukebox and stamp on its silvery plastic innards, splinters of Jamiroquai and Steps flailing into the Hooch-soaked night. Two songs from 1994 save the pub soundtrack: one is about eternal youth, the other about the freedom to love whoever you want.

*

I'm in the loft tapping away on the Canon StarWriter: Mr Robinson's music memoirs have given me a taste for my own zine-writing life. The narrow rectangular screen glows green and across it my eager words appear line by line. I'm describing Blur's 'Girls & Boys' slamming into a bouncing mosh pit at Sheffield Arena. The crowd, from my vantage point, moves like the sea, pogo-ing crowns of sweaty hair surging towards Damon Albarn as he whips his microphone lead against the front of the stage. I am mesmerised by the levitating hamburgers floating above the band. I lap it up when the South Yorkshire crowd boos Damon's description of 'For Tomorrow' as a song about London. I'm gulping in the dry ice and lyrics about wife swapping. Damon is in his Fila zip-top, telling me that love in the '90s is paranoid. He's looking skywards, fluttering his eyelashes. My new favourite song is an ode to shagging holidays in Greece. I don't know what he means, but I want to follow him.

The song at first seems to celebrate sexual choice, maybe even a hymn to bisexuality ('. . . boys like they're girls, who do girls like they're boys'), but the dancefloor is covered in sweat and spilled alcopops, squeaking stickily every time I try to lift my feet. It's synthetic, it's cheap, it's how the '90s feel to me: I'm lost on the edges of the dancefloor in my Adidas Trimm Trabbs, invisible to boys, but believing in myself, bit by bit. I'm making mental notes. Blur, with their clarinet lessons, bowl cuts and beads, have created a parody that merges with provincial-town reality: sickly shots and snogs on black, shiny upholstery. Our town nightclub is called Night Out. Its nickname is Shite Out.

Growing up in the north, Oasis are the chosen ones in 1995's Battle of Britpop. By the time of the August chart showdown between 'Country House' and 'Roll With It', I stand mostly alone in my loyalty to Blur who are too middle-class, too good-looking, too clever, too close to a boy band, but mostly too southern for my friends' approval.

A few years later, in my early twenties, I find myself on a trip to Ayia Napa, the Cypriot town that is overrun by badly behaved Brits each summer. And there I see 'Girls & Boys' with my own eyes. I live the song: I dance on tables, drink sickly sweet spirits and wear a t-shirt that reads 'What happens in Ayia Napa stays in Ayia Napa'. And on the last night, I sleep on a balcony sun-lounger to escape my roommate who is having sex – *in my bed* – with a man she met a few hours ago. I listen to the crickets and stare up into the night sky, wondering how I got lost inside the spoof. *Always should be someone you really love.*

*

Liam Gallagher is in his round John Lennon sunglasses, sat in a chair, up in the air, stuck to a wall. 'Live Forever' is at the sunny, melodic intersection between the decade's new optimism and the peacocking laddish swagger to come. In a sense, it *is* the '90s in one song. A time of forward momentum, a promise of immortality, but still dressed in yesterday's clothes. It might be the sweetest Oasis song. It isn't overplayed like 'Wonderwall', and it doesn't have coke in its nostrils like 'Champagne Supernova'.

In shops, magazines and in my peripheral vision, the cover art of 'Live Forever' keeps drawing me in. I'm stubbornly a Blur fan, but I'm intrigued by the distant nostalgia: a 1930s semi-detached house in the suburbs of an English town or city, framed by fluffy black and white trees, rustling in the breeze of a July day. It is somebody else's sighing summer. Between two brick posts, there's a wrought-iron gate inviting us onto the driveway. It feels safe and familiar, a street we've kicked a deflated football down. But there's also an unreachable, dream-like quality. It is a childhood we remember but can no longer touch. The house in the picture is John Lennon's boyhood home at 251 Menlove Avenue in Liverpool. Coupled with the track's title, it evokes instant melancholia. Once again, I am feeling nostalgic for things I've yet to know.

'We see things they'll never see,' started out as a wistful line, maybe about the idea of living into an endless future but, to me, it is a line that describes the joy of noticing things that seem to pass others by. I sit on trains, with my Walkman on, seeing the sun behind a row of factory buildings outside Doncaster, and – my face reflected in the thick glass – I watch my own film. Oasis's lyric is also a brag used by football fans to wind up rival supporters. You see the words on stickers peppering the London Underground after match days.

They are the words that set up the chorus of 'Live Forever', the jumping-off point. From his chair up in the sky, Liam is questioning himself – 'maybe I just don't believe' – before bringing us, the listener, into his world – 'maybe you're the same as me' – and asking us to feel what he is feeling, which is an agitated sense of hope. We see things others can't see: it's the high expectation of the mid-'90s and, in its poetic arrogance, the phrase contains the true essence of the brothers.

'Live Forever' is the third single from *Definitely Maybe*, the most talked-about debut album of the decade so far. I buy the album furtively on Knaresborough market a few months after its release and for a while I am confused by the cassette inlay because 'Cigarettes and Alcohol', the single that follows 'Live Forever', is listed simply as 'Cigarettes'. And then I notice a sticker on the box which declares it 'for sale in GCC [Gulf Cooperation Council] countries only'. How this copy found its way to the three-quid stall, next to the man my mum buys rhubarb from, we'll never know. I'm steadfastly a Blur fan, but I can't help myself loving the way Liam Gallagher sings 'may-beeeeh' in the opening line of 'Live Forever'. It's every moment of a night out in provincial '90s England rolled into two drawn-out vowels. It's the world I know, just like Lennon's faded suburbia. I stand forever in the morning rain that 'soaks you to the booone' on a piss-wet pavement glistening at the bus stop, fag ends bleeding their brown goo into the cracks as I look down at my dirty Dunlop Green Flash feet.

*

Back in the future, Noel and Liam Gallagher are riding past me on a golf buggy through thousands of Oasis fans who don't notice it's them until they are gone. The brothers are cruising at speed across

Knebworth Park's knobbly grass, which is strewn with plastic cups. Liam is pointing to random people, he shouts something, and now he's throwing his head back in laughter. We see things they'll never see: a glimpse of their own sweaty Adidas disciples.

We have fought to be here through the chugging fumes of hundreds of coaches, lined up side-by-side on dry earth in a universe of stumbling day-trippers. White plastic cords looped between metal poles hem us in, creating a temporary order, as kids in bucket hats trip through queues in search of their own Spike Island. The park's outer edges are soundtracked by Supernova Radio, an Oasis-only zone. I feel both excited and sick, glancing down to check that my shirt's Blur logo is visible. As the lights dip, anticipation rises like cider-flavoured ocean spray from the sea of swaying fans. Liam Gallagher is dressed all in white, like a priest, and first sings his own version of Blur's 'Parklife'. 'All the people, so many people, and we allll go hand in hand,' he slurs, like a drunk man trying to find the coin slot in the jukebox. I look across at my friend Andy and we grin. The crowd surges, the tinder earth scratching the soles of 100,000 trainers. Liam performs his own songs much too fast as he looks out across his never-ending fandom, and so we all sing along at a breathless pace too. 'Wonderwall', over and out in two minutes. Lads in Manchester City shirts flail on shoulders. Girls with sunburn reach to catch a flying drumstick. 'Live Forever', there it is, the anthem of now, maybe of tomorrow, and we sing it like we mean it, as beer sploshes expensively into the dusty dirt. Later we stagger, lost but laughing, inhaling more coach fumes, as we seek the road home back to Yorkshire. I bundle the concert programme to safety, still flat and glossy beneath my Blur shirt with its imaginary perfect castle.

9

Who lives in a house like this?

Some of the groups that I am now devouring are barely disguised
boy band scenesters with more fringes than songs, and I'm delighted.
I have no idea who is snorting coke on the pool table in the Good
Mixer in Camden (a mythological place to me, in the mist beyond

the indie lamppost) and I'm not raging at the sell-out '90s because I'm in my bedroom in North Yorkshire playing my songs to the moon, before going downstairs for tea.

I am not disgusted at the commercialisation of alternative music. I am an eager consumer of it. With the money I make from my Saturday job (£2.50 an hour selling fags and Murray Mints to old ladies), I am glad I can afford the CD version of Blur's 'Charmless Man' as well as the seven-inch with its little gold tab, like a cuff link, which I stop myself from peeling away. I buy the glitter-speckled clear vinyl version of My Life Story's 'Sparkle' (on the cover Jake Shillingford appears as a Man Ray spoof; pearls on his cheeks like tears, a kiss curl, another antidote to the march of the monobrows) and I'm thrilled that Menswear's seven-inch of 'Sleeping In' comes in a plastic see-through bag with two free postcards, which go straight on my wall.

During this phase of feverish acquisition (my shoebox has become a shelf), I subscribe to numerous fanzines that I find advertised in the back of *Melody Maker*. Little A5 booklets arrive in brown envelopes, with cartoons and in-jokes and poorly photocopied images from live shows, the arms and hands of die-hards visible in the lower third, clutching the metal barrier. I love the fanzines that arrive with guitar chord tabs the most, and I begin to pummel my fingertips in pursuit of an indie utopia only reached through these scraps of paper, stapled erratically in someone else's bedroom.

Britpop is already a dirty word, out there, but I am not passed out on Alan McGee's floor (the infamous boss of Creation Records, as remote to me as Mr Tumnus through the wardrobe in Narnia), and I'm not being pushed into the bushes by drunk lads in cagoules doing pretend Mancunian accents.

For me, this deluge of new music is sent from heaven to seek and destroy the sickening dominance of Boyzone and the Outhere Brothers. I hear 'Alright' by Supergrass wafting through the changing rooms in Dorothy Perkins and I smile to myself as Gaz Coombes' fuzzy pianos seem to smash through the gentle – and very boring – clack of plastic clothes hangers being pushed gently by women in search of a holiday dress. When Pulp's 'Sorted for E's and Wizz' lands them in the tabloids ('Ban this sick stunt,' shouts the *Mirror*) for putting a speed wrap diagram on the CD inlay, Claire rushes out to buy the paper as a badge of honour: we are gleeful that *our* bands are sticking it to the mainstream. It's our punk, and we won't be told otherwise.

London – the place I long to be – is turning, but here in Jamiroquai-ridden Knaresborough, I am still Britpop Fan Number One. I turn up the volume on my newest purchase, *Nuisance* by Menswear, bought on 24 October 1995, the day of release. I've ordered the cassette and collect it with pride. The inlay is glossy – so very glossy – and the paper smells expensive: it reminds me of walking through the perfume section of duty free at the airport, a fleeting mood of luxury, an unreachable idea of glamour that fades along a windowless corridor.

Despite its jangly guitars, orchestral strings and references to the 'rat race', 'superficial fuckers' and Camden town (again), the album doesn't really feel like other indie releases. There is nothing DIY here, no mud under the fingernails, no sellotaped mic stands. A sci-fi TV screen glows orange on the cover. It is hyper-real and from another universe, maybe even the future. As I fan out the inlay, black-and-white portraits of Johnny, Chris, Simon, Stuart and Matt look very literally as if they have been photographed for the menswear section of a mail-order clothing catalogue. It is deliberately, deliciously, contrived and beautifully false, like Johnny's perfect Britpop fringe. *Breathe deeper daydreamer*. I know I am dancing inside a mirage.

*

In my head, I'm a rulebreaker like them. In reality, I have handed in my homework on time and I'm polite to Mrs Crebbin who teaches the top set in GCSE maths and sometimes, disconcertingly, appears at my neighbour's house playing whist. We sisters spy her through the window from our back garden wall, which has a dip in it that feels like sitting in a saddle. It's from here that we watch with strange fascination, jumping down frantically through the tall purple arms of the buddleia bush at any sign of her looking up to meet our gaze.

In school, Mrs Crebbin has Magic Eye posters stuck up all around the classroom and when the usual-suspect students – I seem to be surrounded by absolute boffins – finish their work early, she tells them to stare at the walls until they see a leopard emerge. I can never quite do it – too impatient – and in any case, I never get through the work with idle minutes to fill. I am dragged along by the cleverness of my peers, who seem to understand how to factorise an equation or draw a parabola on the first try. I tell myself I am a words person, but there's no time for scrawling lyrics at the back of my exercise book. I have a picture of Johnny Dean inside my English folder alongside a black-and-white shot of a mournful late-career Boris Becker. His big eyelashes seem to sigh, a strange counterpoint to the swagger of Dean and a tug-of-love between the younger and present versions of me. I haven't yet dared paste in a picture of Justine from Elastica.

*

I'm cross at all the journalists telling me my new favourite things are shit. I'm not prepared to believe these weary critics have seen this sort of thing happen before, as they claim, and that it all ends in drugs and tears. I reckon they are jealous because I get to be sixteen during Britpop, while they are all past it in their late twenties. Some of them are even older than the bands themselves. Despite what they say about the fickleness of pop stars invented on a Tuesday afternoon in Soho House (another mystical temple of the south), I remain well up for it, but not 'mad fer it', thank you, because Blur are still better than Oasis and always will be, and you'll see in the end that I'm right. My increasingly forthright views on music are giving me a new confidence in school. I inform the cloakroom that the best band to hail from Liverpool is not actually the Beatles (although they have some good tunes) but it's Space, who are hilarious and clever and sarcastic, and sing about transvestites and Saddam Hussein *in the same verse*. This, my friends, is better than Ronan Keating serenading us about (boring!) love.

Miles away from Camden, Space are asking me 'who lives in a house like this?' In my bedroom, I'm looking across the railway from the window. I like to imagine the characters of my own neighbourhood settling into their nightly routines in the twilight. There's the old lady opposite my granny who keeps her shampoos and toiletries on the mantelpiece. There are the town councillors with bellies held up by invisible belts.

The music press is sniffy about the psychedelic world of Space, but I inhale their chemical colours and enjoy the pantomime. 'Neighbourhood' mashes together B-movie synths with Halloween spookiness and a faux Ennio Morricone western sound: a techni-coloured *OK Corral* effect at the end of each chorus. The mood is one of mischief, a trippy soap opera of kick-ass angels and misfits. As the saloon doors fling open, there's an alien Scouser stood there, grinning, with a tin of baked beans and a copy of *Woman's Weekly*.

Space are one of the bands on the edges of the mid-'90s indie boom, and therefore more immune to both its false inflation and its eventual downfall (Space keep going into the 2000s, Menswear vanish and return when everyone has forgotten about them with a strange Japan-only second album). I use their angular oddness in arguments at school, copy their snarls in the mirror, look for their haircuts among the boys I'd like to look back at me. More than anything, I'm just so relieved to listen to songs about topics other than unrequited love.

I look at myself and see a skinny, flat-chested girl still waiting for *things to happen*. Claire gets to go to gigs for real, in York and Leeds, and comes back with tales of Elastica playing a few feet away on a tiny stage in a venue called Fibbers. Another night she gets a hand slap from Kula Shaker frontman Crispian Mills. I continue to build my pop world at the top of the house. My room is still a mish-mash of toys and clothes that don't fit me anymore: Screwball Scramble, which I'm too good at, plastic boxes of old Lego, a tub of little green soldiers dusted in soil from a bygone garden trench, my first-year school kilt still hanging over the banister, the Sunday dress that I'll never wear again, and my Dunlop Green Flash trainers repainted white, awaiting a bright tennis day. I am all these characters: the tomboy, the sporty one, the girl with legs long enough for any dress. It's *me* who lives in a house like this.

*

The Britpop naysayers – music writers, mostly, and occasionally my teachers (my music teacher refuses to believe Blur's 'The Universal' is my favourite song) – have missed an important point. It's the vivid colours of the scene – in some cases, literally the red, white and blue of our queasy flag – that lead me, and other trainee music anoraks, to the leaf greens, dusty purples and twinkly yellows of previous music waves, from '60s pop to punk and shoegaze. Menswear and Space might be the cameo jokers, but they show me that music is sometimes meant to be ridiculous, like an inside-out house. Art itself becomes the topic of mainstream chatter: Rachel Whiteread's inverted home, Tracey Emin's bed and Damien Hirst's sheep are the physical manifestations of Britain's new love-hate relationship with the absurd. We are all on a hurtling dodgem at the seaside now, but finally the soundtrack is mine. Damon Albarn is the reason I know about Ray Davies and the Kinks, Jarvis Cocker educates me about Scott Walker, Elastica expertly thieve their scruffy leathers from Wire and the Fall, while Lush usher me down a grassy pathway, thick with dandelions and reverb pedals, to Strawberry Switchblade and My Bloody Valentine. This sort of thing simply doesn't happen with the new Peter Andre single.

10

Only girl in the record shop

Air rushes across my cheeks as I sprint towards the playing fields. I'm out of control and skidding down the grassy embankment behind the EMF railings, my Adidas feet scuffling for control. I use my downhill momentum to get me up the other side, running past the smokers' woods, the snogging hedge, away, and beyond Mr Robinson's portacabin across the athletics track, with its worn white lines, where I won the 800 metres on sports day in the second year. That Friday, three years ago, I raised my arms in weary victory as I hobbled over the finishing line and in that spliced moment between relief and joy, I revealed unshaved armpits. My sister, a sixth former, shot me a look. Not yet daring to borrow my mum's razor, I was hairy for the first time and had done nothing about it. I folded my Airtex arms – and the moment – away.

This time, as I stop to catch my breath in the August air, buzzing with insects and the anticipation of the day, I'm breathing deeply in a different way. I know I will think of this moment in the future. *On a day like today, nothing gets better, come what may.* I've just picked up my GCSE results: a clean sweep of A's, humorously tainted by a D in computer studies. After all the hours revising with my guitar and The La's, the all-nighters listening to the Beatles greatest hits tape copied from the library, the half-drunk hot drinks with their layer of Rich Tea sludge, I've done it. This part of things is over. I'm vaulting away from double maths and hockey, forever, towards gigs and festivals and charity-shop treasure and people who will break my heart, and others who will remake it. When I get home, breathless, Mum is in the kitchen, ever so slightly on tenterhooks. She smiles with her usual big-eyed kindness and her shoulders drop with relief and pride at my news. She gives me a crisp ten-pound note and I know exactly how I will spend it.

I reach up to the 'B' section on the squeaky carousel, inhaling the smell of old carpet and mice, so familiar now, as I spool through rotating cassettes along Heapy's right-hand wall. I pull down Blur's 'Parklife', mine at last. A song about the shipping forecast. The mystery of a speeding car. Graham rolling a fag. My shoebox tape collection is mostly made up of singles, with albums borrowed and bootlegged. A carefully photocopied cover – those greyhounds, forever in motion – I now have in colour. In a couple of weeks, in the heat of summer, Blur will win the Battle of Britpop when 'Country House' beats Oasis's 'Roll With It' to number one. I buy the *NME* with its 'British Heavyweight Championship' cover, Damon side-eyeing his prize beside Liam in shades, turning, as if to shout a Burnage expletive over his shoulder. Blur are billed as the teen-girl choice, which annoys me, but then I'm already a girl in a boys' world, trying to fit in as I search through the singles racks in Leeds shops like Polar Bear and Jumbo Records. I'm judging everything by its cover, because that's all I can do. I carry a list of artists I've read about in the *NME*, or heard a snatch of on the radio. Ash, 'Oh Yeah'. Mono, 'Life in Mono'. Dubstar, 'Stars'.

*

Cerys Matthews is sitting at the top of an old Edwardian lamppost, her legs astride its lantern, high in the sky. She's on Arthur Street where a black and white cat is missing. 'Lost Cat' finds me when I am meant to be revising, but instead I've wandered up to the market place. As I pick up the CD single, its creamy fabric inlay feels good in my hands. I buy it for a pound. The cover art reminds me of Picasso's *Weeping Woman*, which I've been copying from a book in the art room at school, and it seems to me that Catatonia fit alongside bands like the Divine Comedy and Tindersticks. I like the songs at the edges of Britpop, with violins, flowers and chipped nail varnish, and I sense I should follow them.

*

Music fandom sends me on strange quests. I listen to new albums *until* I like them. I write to fanzines asking them for guidance: Which album by the Smiths should I start with? (*Hatful of Hollow*, a helpful reply tells me, in neat biro.) I hunt down Blur's mysterious outtakes and B-sides – 'People in Europe', 'Peter Panic', 'Young and Lovely' – via friendly strangers who also subscribe to the fanclub magazine, *Blurb*. I'm wildly jealous of those who were members in time to get the enamel badge of the train on the cover of *Modern Life is Rubbish*. I steal Dad's *Record Collector* magazines and buy unofficial recordings from recent but already legendary gigs: Blur at Mile End (in the distant capital city, forever calling me) in the dry June of 1995 and the near-mythical Sugary Tea Tour of 1993. My fingertips are sore from the fretboard on a lefty guitar. I've learned to play 'This is a Low'.

Heapy's record shop has a metal trolley around the back where old posters are dumped for the binmen. There's a furtive thrill in rifling through piles of damp cardboard in the hope of digging out an uncrumpled poster. I'm forever chasing the first high – a pop-up hexagon to promote Liverpool's FA Cup song, 'Anfield Rap' – but now there are more bands to follow, I spy new opportunities every week. My eyes are tuned, this time for the curve of the lower case 'b' in Blur. I find Marion brooding in glossy black beneath a flattened box. Under black bags holding a rainwater reservoir, I glimpse a tree on a distant horizon. It leads me to a falsetto boy and a band called Geneva.

*

Singer Andrew Montgomery's vowels seem to arc through space, unlike any voice I've heard before. I'm back at the window where I used to climb from as a child. Mum never knew about the dangerous adventures out onto the slates, my feet dangling across dark grey squares, my fingers gripping the edge of the frame. It was only ever a dare on hot summer's days. This same window, just like 'Strawberry Fields Forever', when I was eleven, is the gateway to the feelings that music brings me – and will always bring me. I'm trembling in their company, offering myself into their emotional arms, always wondering who it is that I am meant to be, and who I might meet in my life with whom to share these feelings. This music connects me to the most unknown part of my heart. At school, I'm still the one who cracks the jokes, the one who finds a way to break the awkward moments. But this version of me at the window, nobody yet knows.

Just like this part of my inner world, nobody else seems to notice Geneva. And yet they are the best new band in the world. I've started my journey to the verges of the scene and soon I'll defend this verdant turf, with its jewels of rain, its beetle pathways and its muddy fingernails, because Britpop's also-rans feel more *mine*. I realise that I want to walk the pavements of East Kilbride with Geneva, just me and them. I am tasting the raindrops still bouncing from the poster that bears their name, only for me. Other bands join me on the kerb but it's this song, bought cheaply from the reject pile, that connect me to emotions I've never felt before: longing, the hope of someone catching me, the joy of being on the edge.

*

On the last day of school, we spill out of the clunking year 11 doors, under the bridge from senior school to the computer wing, where I will soon sit my German oral test in a strange cube-like room, my kindly teacher Miss Smith gesturing wildly but silently to encourage me as the tape recorder whirrs. I feel a rush of love for her, an unprocessed mini crush. Back in the yard, in the haze of shirt signings, a wave of kissing sweeps through the bobbing crowd of greasy teenage heads, our version of midnight on New Year's Eve. Deano plants his lips very briefly on my mouth, we smile, and I kiss him back with cautious lips. It's different from our usual French class chats about the whereabouts of his ruler and his dented Toon Army pencil tin.

We merge over the road, shirts hanging over grey trousers and kilts, ties worn as bandanas, bags slung low. A group of us – an unusual configuration of nearly-friends – decide to go down to Knaresborough House, a former stately home, now a council building, at the bottom of the high street. In its grounds it has a well-tended garden, high old walls and a hill where children sledge in the winter. Our white nylon school shirts flutter in the optimistic air of early May, covered in the names of our friends, their signatures in black marker pen and biro. We dump our bags and roll down curved humps of green, unbothered by grass stains on our elbows and knees, a gentle two-fingers to our compulsory school years. In my heart, I know things will never be quite the same.

My older sister Claire goes to gigs that I am still too young-looking to be sure of entering. I eagerly await news of her adventures instead. I return to the loft and push my calloused fingers onto my guitar's fretboard – C–G–D – in search of a Shakespeare quote, all memorised this way. In between atoms and verbs and Macbeth, I dream of the tree surrounded by pale blue and the horizon.

Secret track 2

She's my sister

With Kerstin at Blur in Hyde Park in 2009. (Photo: Liza Brett)

The bands we love often sing about sisters. Pulp have the Sisters *EP that contains the single 'Babies', and its lyrics about the wardrobe and the girl with boys in her room. The way Ian Brown says 'She's my sister' on 'Love Spreads' always finds me in the heart, and it might be the most interesting thing about the song. Saint Etienne's 'Sylvie' comes closer to the bone – 'Sylvie, girl, although you're my little sister, Well you're not without your charms' – but, in truth, we three never compete and certainly not for the same boy.*

    Claire is the oldest, our musical leader and chief magpie, gleaning information about gigs and new music and release dates from Melody Maker. *She receives cryptic messages in the mail from Alex at* Pulp People: *hand-posted cards arrive with mysterious artwork and a few teasing words, much of it inspired by the estates around Sheffield. The whole city is your jewellery box. We obsess together over the weird names – Wombwell, Catcliffe, The Wicker – and feel the same about the grazes that fade on summer knees. Claire delights in the cut 'n' paste scrapbook of homespun glamour in the fanzine* Disco Very *and, overnight, switches from a gentle hippy-ish style – flowing skirts and neckerchiefs – to knitted tank tops and pencil skirts. She never peels the sticker on the I Spy programme handed to fans at Pulp's V96 Warrington concert. I sit on the wall in the garden by the buddleia, listening to her describe the feeling of being at the front, just a touch away from Jarvis in his crushed-velvet jacket.*

Kerstin is our little sister, four years behind me and nine behind Claire. This means that in our sibling version of the Battle of Britpop, Blur and Pulp are already 'taken'. Oasis are off the table – we are all trainee music snobs and find their songs too simplistic for our poetic temperaments – and so Kerstin chooses

the Charlatans instead and develops cute little Tim Burgess-y tics: the way he says 'in the rain' at a live show, his Cheshire vowels amusing her, and the way he stands at the microphone, his Adidas Sambas splayed in a Liam Gallagher way but he seems so much sweeter. We watch the video for 'How High' together on the Chart Show *on a Saturday morning and imagine ourselves flying through the hyper-real forest in quest of Tim in his yellow cagoule. Kerstin is eating a bowl of Lucky Charms, bought in a little individual box from Spar. She is resourceful and often sorts out her own food supply. Sometimes, when she arrives home from school feeling hungry and sees nothing she likes in the fridge, she rolls up her bottle-green cuffs and makes a quiche before settling down to* Heartbreak High.

I am visiting Kerstin's new bedroom, which is now beyond the bathroom in the furthest flung part of the house, our granny's room for a while and still smelling of her hand cream. Kerstin has recently moved here because I am seventeen and have bullishly declared that I need the loft all to myself for important activities such as listening to the Manic Street Preachers. The toys are all gone anyway – the purple-haired Swan Keyper with its tiny pink comb and paper notes, Kerstin's well-curated Barbie dolls with their various beauty accessories – all packed away to be found in a flurry of nostalgia sometime in the future. Now, when I visit Kerstin down the hall, she is playing Tellin' Stories *on her CD player, beneath a shelf of Coca-Cola bottles with their necks pulled and contorted in glass loops. She is a teenager now and getting secretive.*

11

Begone Gareths, hello Nicky

I finally look old enough to go clubbing in our neighbouring town. I've let my ponytail out and put on silver-grey eyeshadow and black eyeliner. Really, I want to cut my hair short, like Justine from Elastica, but I haven't plucked up the courage yet and I know Mum will not be keen. Jenny, my friend since junior school, has acquired the perfect Britpop haircut, almost by accident: an asymmetric swoosh of glossy fringe, and beneath it dark brown eyes. I am envious and taking notes. Jimmy's in Harrogate is a hangout for sixth-form girls and famed for the upside-down Mini Cooper suspended precariously over the main stairway. Older men, called Gareth, Jamie and Luke, surround us on entry. We are watched like fresh chicks trying out our new wings.

I don't expect to hear any music that I truly like, but I have little soft spots for the fairground rush of Strike's 'U Sure Do', 'Not Over Yet' by Grace and Corona's 'Baby Baby'. Even Whigfield's 'Saturday Night'. There's a serotonin momentum in these plasticky songs that sound the way lemon Hooch tastes; a fake citrus tang that sends me onto the dancefloor against my indie-snob better judgement. But after a while it happens. The opening strings of 'Something Good' by Utah Saints reach me at the bar, where I am spending the first £1.20 of the ten pounds in my purse. Half a cider is swiftly abandoned. The track's frantic lyrics – 'Utah Saints! U-U-U-Utah Saints!' – propel me across a sticky dancefloor circled by Gareths in untucked shirts and smart shoes, the men that girls in provincial towns must constantly negotiate. The song interrupts the smooth-edged handbag house with a cartoon anarchy, and I push through the fug of Lynx Africa to take my place.

We girls stay together with a series of unspoken but understood rules, and the very certain knowledge that we will end the night together eating a cheeseburger and chips from the tiny fast-food window opposite the bus station. We visit the loo in twos and keep together in the bar queue; Yorkie with her wallet on a chain like a skater girl, me with a deliberately twee purse patterned with translucent butterflies. None of us is allowed to leave without telling the others, and the call sign goes up if one of us is missing for more than half an hour. If this happens, we hoist up our All Saints combat trousers and set off to scour the tacky leather booths, wary that one of our mates could be obscured from view by a deceptively handsome Gareth. We wear tight tops and keep everything we need for the night stashed in our huge Nicole Appleton pockets: purse, lighter, gum, ten Marlboro Lights. Jenny wears a black strappy vest, Julie's in shiny lip gloss, Hélène is in her Pulpy striped top and throwing her head back in laughter like she always does, and Kim, the EMF girl, is the only one in a dress; black and tight, with bangles. Yorkie's in massive Vans trainers, way bigger than her actual feet, and I am in my Menswear 'Daydreamer' t-shirt with a deconstructed Mini on the front, in the style of a Haynes car manual. We all smell of Impulse and spearmint Extra.

There is no indie room and the DJs are always men. Nobody questions this, but my steady diet of *Melody Maker* – written by old-school socialists who rage at the inequality of everything and encourage boys into eyeliner (and soon I do too) – means I've at least inwardly thought 'I could do so much better'.

*

I am watching Utah Saints snake in silhouette through the back corridors of a giant concert venue. They move in slow motion but there's a flailing punk mood, a sweaty, bare-chested energy. Four years before this moment, I'm sitting in my pyjamas on Saturday morning, my sisters either side, and pleased to see that 'Something Good' is in the *Chart Show*'s dance chart. Utah Saints are from our neighbouring town, Harrogate. The video splices in footage from Kate Bush's 'Cloudbusting', the cute, burbling sample at the heart of the song, and then Kate herself appears with short, choppy hair, meandering down a country lane in a cardigan. London streets shimmer in fast forward. Kate glances upwards, as if bemused to find herself in a speeding chart-rave tune that might incite teenage girls to maraud a northern dancefloor.

There's a thunderbolt wrestling me free. Keyboards burst into waterfalls. I'm falling in love with the chaotic euphoria, the sweat, the unsmart shoes. I dance with freedom as the song connects me to future nights out in which I will venture alone through rumbling rooms, in a haze, knowing my friends are freewheeling through all this too. There will be hand massages from strangers, a Buffalo shoe incident on the stairs, a damp combat hem in a chill-out puddle, and a landline number written on the cardboard stub from a packet of Rizlas.

*

It's the farm boys who introduce me to the Manic Street Preachers. Patrick makes me a tape of his favourite tracks from *Generation Terrorists* and *Gold Against the Soul*. He has older brothers who know about music, and he has hand-picked a playlist that starts with 'La Tristessa Durera', 'Motorcycle Emptiness' and 'Little Baby Nothing'. I am sitting on a high hay bale, looming over the farmyard, clutching a two-litre bottle of Strongbow, contemplating both these songs and the moon. I lean forwards, slightly unsteady, and rest my arm on a tall, woodworm-ravaged rail that skirts the stairs up into the barn. My friends are sitting in a circle to my left, sparking up the dog-ends of a spliff. The balustrade moves a little and I take away my weight, before watching it collapse and fall elegantly into the farmyard. The cider whooshes to my head, I'm embarrassed and horrified, instantly sober. Splinters of wood smack down to the ground missing two of my friends' cars by centimetres. I lurch to say sorry. Patrick says his dad's been expecting this for a while. We put on 'Life Becoming a Landslide' and it seems to fit the moment.

Year 12 has changed our social hierarchies. New boys arrive from village schools that don't have sixth forms and we town girls have adopted them. This influx gives us new freedom because the farm boys have their own cars, which take us on risky late-night journeys along narrow country lanes. We speed between high hedges, numbed to the dangers of the dark by the rasp of James Dean Bradfield's vowels or a deep, leather-upholstered techno beat. The boys we've grown up with must take a temporary back seat.

I am one of the newly assembled gang. Craig runs the vending machine and covertly deals us black-market sweets. I share a locker with Hélène, where we keep a bottle of apple Tango that we slurp between lessons. We spend free periods in the study room, which is in a converted loft. Not much studying happens but other things happen under the eaves, usually involving a new boy. At lunchtime, we walk to the market place because we can, and queue up for sandwiches in Prudames, which feels grown-up. I'm still finding myself through music and the Manics allow me to adopt a new kind of confidence. I start wearing eyeliner at school and try to understand the lyrics enough to quote them. I scrawl 'assassinated beauty' on my English folder.

At last, I am the girl down the front. I've wriggled forward to the first three rows and if I stretch my fingers, I can touch the barrier.

CONNECTION IS A SONG

I've taken my place just as the lights dip and I am perfectly placed in front of Nicky Wire's bass guitar. I'm in my sister's fake fur coat, which is very hot. When the band stride onto stage, I feel a surge of hotter bodies behind me. My head fills with a rush of white noise. Nicky spreads his Wales flag across a wardrobe-sized amplifier as I sweep uncontrollably forwards with the strangers around me: we are all fur and feathers, a sweaty smudge of eye make-up and biro'd lyrics, a clutching mass of scuffing feet lifting from the floor. There's no real choice, and so I let my body flail into the dark mass. I'm no longer in control as Nicky scissor-kicks towards me and throws his black feather boa into dozens of outstretched hands, one of them mine. There's another surge of smothering heat as I enter a muffled underworld – all by myself – my friends, so far away now. A blackness descends.

Traci Lords, the female voice of 'Little Baby Nothing', was nearly Kylie Minogue. Richey Edwards had wanted the Australian pop star to represent vulnerable innocence on his dark duet about the sex industry's 'loveless slavery'. But they couldn't get Kylie at the time (they did eventually perform and record with her years later) and so Richey instead developed a fascination with Lords, an American porn actress. The song was released in November 1992, a few months after Utah Saints' 'Something Good', but from another time and space. When I first hear it on the farm, it feeds my desire for a rallying cry against everything, but especially capitalism, as I clutch my cider and crisps, bought from the garage. 'Little Baby Nothing', just those three words alone, sounds like a gothic short film and I have to know more.

I am listening to Patrick's tape on my Walkman. Like its sibling 'Motorcycle Emptiness', 'Little Baby Nothing' stands out from the wiry, punk-metal tracks on *Generation Terrorists*. It soars angrily but melodically through ever-ascending phases, a kind of multi-chorus orgy about the destruction of purity in the name of money. In the track's promo video, directed by the *NME*'s Steven Wells, a black-vested James Dean Bradfield spits out the song inside a slogan-daubed studio. 'All rock 'n' roll is homosexual,' it says above his head. 'Culture, alienation, boredom and despair.' An actress mimes Lords' lines, with 'read my lips' written along her thigh in red lipstick.

Propped up against the back wall of Doncaster Dome, I am just waking up from my journey into unconsciousness. In my hand, I find that I am clutching a bottle of water, but I don't know who gave it to me. My head feels papery, but I can hear the band: a distant, kaleidoscopic dream of 'Motorcycle Emptiness'. I look down and see that I am covered in black feathers. I've missed the gig, but I seem to have these holy relics.

They are Nicky's feathers.

12

I'm waiting for you

'The first time you see yourself naked, you cry,' sings James Dean Bradfield on 'Faster' and I think of myself in a child's vest at PE, shoulders hunched, strangely ashamed to be tall. I suppress waves of these feelings about who I am, and who I might become, and I send them back into the sky, the pinks and yellows of my favourite songs now blue and grey in the glass layers of my window. I look at the gap between the glazing and imagine myself trapped there, safe like a plastic figure in a snow globe, able to see outside, but pinned down, contained. I am warm and sleepy here, but I know I must shake myself into the world.

I am listening to my special edition CD of the Manic Street Preachers' *Generation Terrorists*, which has a repeating image of Christ in a crown of thorns across the disc: a weeping and forsaken big-eyed Messiah, looking upwards eternally. Richey Edwards' lacerating lyrics spray me like tiny beads of blood and sweat; his self-loathing finding every tributary into my increasingly self-critical teenage mind. I look in the mirror and see a dark skyline. I hate my crooked teeth. My hands don't fit my arms. I want my friend's Britpop fringe, but my hair curls away from the thought.

Despite my increasingly dystopian tendencies, a band that sings 'pour your misery down on me' seems too blatant with its bleakness, and so I scoff a little at my friend Yorkie's new obsession, Garbage. Now that I'm an absolute music snob, I declare 'I'm Only Happy When It Rains' to be lightweight and continue to grapple instead with the Manics and their lyrics about capitalism, drug abuse, anorexia and abortion. But I trust Yorkie, who is in a band and plays guitar. Her giant skater shoes (Vans, always new ones with enormous fat tongues) seem to enter the room before her skinny frame, which is angular and cool, fortified only by Pepsi and Marlboro Lights. Yorkie represents the alternative scene in my school, almost single-handedly. She has a huge Kurt Cobain poster in her bedroom and various *Star Wars* models on a shelf, now gathering dust. Her band, Emulsion, plays in the main hall, S1, at lunchtimes and we all stand still as we watch, because any sort of dancing feels like a risk. Teachers pop by and nod along to Yorkie's deliberately abrasive chords. I shrink away from their misunderstanding of the situation.

*

I've changed my mind about Garbage. Shirley Manson's minor chords have bundled me into the back of a speeding car that is travelling towards the hinterlands of my mind, and all because of one song: 'Milk'. And it's only now, many months after Yorkie's recommendation, that I am discovering the tidal wave of emotion hidden on the album's last track. Tears will bring me home, Manson promises, but the route seems dimly lit.

I buy 'Milk' on CD single and play it on repeat in my bedroom. I find myself falling into a dream-like state as I listen, almost intoxicated, and connecting to a sensation that there are people beyond my hometown that are feeling this too. I binge-listen twenty times in a row, drifting off into semi-sleep. The vocal always wakes me with a jolt, as if I've time-travelled into adult life, only to be catapulted back here. 'I'm waiting, I'm waiting for you,' she sings with a piercing, pleading beauty. The song does things to me that I can't yet compute. I have no idea what these lyrics really mean, or what they mean to Manson, but the waiting – waiting, w-a-i-t-i-n-g – seems to be a warning about my own future; the avenues I must travel, the connections I will make, the people I must try to find, the patience I will need. I already knew I was waiting for *something*. This song tells me that I am waiting not to be looked at, but to be *seen*. I want to look deeply into your eyes and for you to hold my gaze. I want to be *the one*. At school, I am still an extra to the circles of power and flirtation; I am swotty but quick-witted, boyish with a hint of brown eyeliner. I'm still waiting for my first, proper, kiss.

*

I first think I might be in love at the age of nine, lying on my sledge looking into the sky at the back of Knaresborough House on a school snow day. My sisters have set off home, pulling the other sledge back to our house along Raw Gap, the most comically named offshoot of the high street. Unlike the plastic trays of our peers, our sledges are proper Scandinavian-style toboggans, the type you see on Christmas cards. A seat, a ride, a snow hammock. At this moment, as I lie backwards, making myself weak to the winter air,

I've deliberately stayed alone, planning one last ride down the hill, but also because I want to be with my thoughts, staring into the heavy sky. Fresh snow falls and I let the delicate flakes spangle onto my tongue. I'm thinking about my school friend and how she makes a swooshing feeling roll through my heart.

This same feeling follows me through school but I bury it, first under heaps of old snow that same winter, adding new powder when dark grit starts showing through the ice. Later, I put this feeling inside a football and kick it as hard as I can into the air, half revelling in the shooting pain it sends through my toe. As summers pass, these thoughts trickle alongside me, a woodland stream that I can't see in the undergrowth but a sound that I can always hear. I cover up the noise by stamping my feet on the pebbles, then running with a stick through tall rustling grasses. But the voice in my head is always there, among the chiffchaffs and the rumbling sky.

In the end, I let pop music fling open its doors.

*

Mansun are a Britpop group that I've pushed into my mind's snobbish margins, spoilt by the rush of choice. My harsh assessment is that Paul Draper's eyelinered eyes are trying too hard in a pop world already occupied by the pretty boys of Suede, Marion and Longpigs. But then 'Wide Open Space' hits me. And, like 'Milk', it hints at a coming era of suppressed love and yearning, of swooping ravens and danger. It appears on the *Four* EP and reveals itself to me like a forbidden jewel in the CD bargain bin. I make it mine for a pound.

Queerness is at the margins of Britain's '90s music boom, having spent the '80s front and centre. The Pet Shop Boys are still cool and cited as an influence by many of my new favourite bands, but the overt celebration of sexual freedom, writ large by the likes of Frankie Goes to Hollywood, Bronski Beat and Erasure, has been replaced in the mainstream by something coy. Brett Anderson says he's bisexual but has never had a homosexual experience. The journalists at *Melody Maker* keep trying to resurrect the blouse-wearing propensities of the New Romantics: there is a brief scene called Romo in the late '90s, but it crashes headfirst into Boots' make-up counter. The women try harder: Garbage have a song called 'Queer', Debbie from Echobelly is openly lesbian. But being a bit gay is largely a Bowie-ish plaything for the boys of Britpop: Johnny from Menswear with his red fringe, Jarvis's hip-swinging pout, Mansun's dash of eyeshadow. Damon and Justine are the dream couple of indie, in the tabloids as much as the *NME*, always falling out of London parties in Adidas tops, each as pretty as the other. But the dominant force is Oasis, whose followers pull up their zips beneath their chins and make anyone *not like them* feel nervous, their bow-legged swagger the only way to survive in a northern town. A boy flicking his cigarette with a painted nail needs to watch his back. There are none of these boys in my school anyway (and if there are, they don't come to the pub). Being female offers some shelter, but to the lads with their sideburns and splayed feet, I feel increasingly invisible in my brown corduroys.

With Richey Manic still in my head (another half-hearted bisexual), I decide I want to wear a mod-style leather jacket that I've found abandoned in my sister's wardrobe. I imagine it will make me look like a lost member of Elastica. I want to cut my hair short too, but that must wait. Still. Mum says that I 'don't want to give the wrong impression'.

*

My first real kiss is about to happen in the castle grounds, tucked away beyond the Cross Keys' beer garden and next to the public toilets. He's a boy from Ripon with blond curtains across his forehead. He's gentle and holds my hand, walking me around the corner and away from view. I don't really know why I'm here, though, beneath a young silver birch tree, about to push my mouth towards a person I hardly know. It's like he just wants to tick it off his list too. Our tongues touch and I go with it. It is mechanical and circular, a washing-machine kiss. He reaches for my ponytail and pulls out my hair. I recoil, a bit shocked: I didn't expect him to do that. I fasten my hair back into place and ask him to buy me half a cider. He smiles and we walk back around to the pub, our friends pretending not to look. Mansun come onto the jukebox. 'Wide Open Space', there it is. I am full of a new sensation: that my real life is out there, but that I must go somewhere else to find it. I will have to keep going, to stay in my head. One day, my love will burst out of me like a spring bud unfurling.

13

Yes, I do feel better

I try to lift my head, but it's no use. Another sickening wave rides through me, my tastebuds rippled with the violent flavour of cider. It scorches my throat, fizzes repulsively over my tongue. I'm disgusted with myself, wishing my friends would be less caring, willing them to leave me here outside the Cross Keys, wretchedly sick and drunk and deservedly, stupidly alone. Vomit streaks from the corner of my mouth and through the slats of the wooden picnic bench where I'm hunched, onto my shiny new Adidas trainers. I really hate myself. Hélène and Jenny sit at my side, rubbing my back, telling me to stop trying to apologise, just to focus on the task of puking. They want me to drink a lukewarm pint of water, but I hate everything and tell them so. I'm wrecked and everything's a spinning blur, and yet I still manage to see them exchange a Lineker '90 look of grave concern. I know I'm Gazza, a weeping mess who needs an early bath.

I attempt to raise my head again and hear the laughter at the start of the Spice Girls' 'Wannabe'. Is it Mel B or Geri? Even in my current state, I want to know the answer. A stomping but fuzzy version of the intro travels to me from the jukebox, Sporty Spice's vocal curving out through the darkly lacquered wooden doors, into the humid night air, past the Ben Sherman lads, through the fog of hairspray, to me on the splintery bench, where I am a lost cause. I'm listening from another world, trying to get back to the place where I know I should be: the fizzy, upward hours before we dance. I beam a drunken grin to my two friends, and give in. My head bangs back down onto the puke-spattered table.

A couple of hours later, I wake to find I am in my own bed and it's still before midnight. I can vaguely remember being handed back to Mum at the back door. Chills of shame. I roll onto my side, realise I'm still in the t-shirt I'd chosen for my failed night out, pale yellow with embossed '70s-style lettering in brown; something the bass player might wear, in my head, but far too short to be a nightie. My mouth still tastes of sick and my heart lurches when my brain delivers me the twin horrors of embarrassment – oh God, so terribly mortifyingly, ciderfully so – and the hurt of missing out on Friday night. They'll be dancing by now. Abba will be playing, 'Dancing Queen' and the line about being seventeen. *Our* line, but I'm not there. I reach for my box of tapes, knowing already which song I need to hear before I dissolve back to sleep.

*

I don't even own the official release of 'Yes' by McAlmont and Butler. I've captured it – and it has captured me – via a free cassette on the cover of *Vox* magazine. It is beautifully sandwiched between Pulp's 'Sorted for E's and Wizz' and Radiohead's 'Nice Dream' on *The Class of '95*, which is possibly the greatest free tape of the '90s (and also features Bjork's 'Hyper-ballad', PJ Harvey's 'Down by the Water' and the Verve's 'History', which I declare to be their best song, as ever, cruelly overlooked). 'Yes' conjures up the defiant emotions inside a break-up – in this case, painful exits by the duo from their respective bands, Suede and Thieves. Butler originally intended 'Yes' to be an instrumental,[i] but then heard McAlmont's voice and imagined how it might add the fine gold leaf to a song he had been privately crafting. When McAlmont talked about his

---

[i] Apparently, before McAlmont, Butler was in early talks to record the song with a well-known 'big name' in the British music establishment, but got annoyed at suggested changes and then backed out. Butler has never confirmed who was in the frame, but Morrissey was rumoured. It's strange to imagine that alternative life for the song. I choose instead to dream of Dusty Springfield in her twilight years, dressed up and shimmering, launching herself at the chorus, flaming the demons from her own life and career. She feels well enough to tell you what you can do.

love of Dusty Springfield and '60s girl groups, the deal was sealed. In my room, rewinding my tape repeatedly, I find it to be a majestic heel-turning rebound of a song. Despite my heartbreaks still being mostly abstract, and hidden, I feel spiritually connected to the fuck you-ness of it all. Yes, I *do* feel better. It is a song meant to be sung through tears.

David McAlmont has a voice as tall as a cathedral and on this song it soars through centuries of heartbreak up to the dusty gargoyles, beyond the untrodden walkways high up where medieval architects left their chisels. The melody is one that it is hard to believe didn't exist before (why didn't Burt Bacharach find these notes first?) with its flying buttress strings and heavenly vocal arches. I know that 'Yes' is a soaring pop masterpiece, one that even my dad would approve of, and yet it still gets lost in the rubble of Britpop: it's never on the jukebox in the Keys, or any pub in Knaresborough, never the last song, only in my room. I know I'll need to get a train just to hear it out loud in public, but in Leeds and York, I still look too young to be sure of getting into a bar. And so, I must wait in sickly seas of 'Cotton Eye Joe'.

The only concessions to even mildly alternative music in my town seem to be 'Wonderwall' by Oasis, Pulp's 'Common People' (although Jarvis Cocker would still get his glasses smashed up by the bins) and 'The Riverboat Song' by Ocean Colour Scene, which is everywhere and, to me, smells of farts and Superdrug aftershave. We girls shelter in safety with the Spice Girls and All Saints, with me always sceptical at the edge of the dancefloor. 'Yes' has powers that draw me to both darker and brighter places, and I play it all the time in my head. I want to stub out my Marlboro Light and walk away, my shoe sole grinding into a gritty pavement, a glint of necklace on my collarbone. I want to flick my fringe and depart, the whole pub watching my exit. It's just that right now, no one would notice. So, instead, I go home and play music loudly into the sky.

Throwing open my blind, I turn up the volume and let the music take me over. Like many of my window songs, it is a track that makes me look upwards, as if the future might be visible if I lift my chin. I gaze past the criss-cross of television aerials and into dark clouds. Something flits by in my peripheral vision; swifts, chattering on the wing, or bats circling the chimney. I love this song because it doesn't fit in. This beautiful male falsetto comes from another universe and, in its five minutes, it both drips with rage and offers renewal. The track is not 'mad fer it'. It is mad *because* of it. Butler, to me, is rejecting the gloss of fame, the Brit Awards, the *NME* covers, the chance to be heard in a pub where thirty-year-old men wear too much hair gel and try to pull my school friends. Through ascending violins, and in McAlmont's almost agitated vocal, I hear them call my name. When I am smarting from another teenage hurt triangle, it is 'Yes' that I fall back on, delivering me drunk but combative into darkness. I am framed by moonlit silver edges, alone again, considering how I might follow the bats to wherever it is they go.

*

The Cross Keys is our place of Friday celebration: a tenner in my pocket, a weekend spring in my step, the hope of a free pool table. For what seems like a whole summer – seven weeks at number one (bookended by Gary Barlow and Peter Andre, I spit this fact to my friends with disgust but they just shrug) – the Spice Girls soundtrack the start of our journeys into inebriation. *Top of the Pops* has moved to Fridays and so 'Wannabe', always at the end of the show, is the song often playing as I put on my make-up: grey eyeshadow, black eyeliner and mascara. Its stomping certainty drives me forwards, I want to be like Mel C: kicking out into the night with a tracksuited leg.

We love the message in the song: boys beware, our friends come first. In Jimmy's, in the Cross Keys, in Shite Out, we care most of all about each other. There are dramas and disappearances. Kim's gone AWOL in the sofa area, Yorkie's phrase 'I'm not well' becomes a 20th-century meme, Hélène's chatting to a random by the loos, and Jenny's at the bar with a rum and coke and the boy she fancies. My hands are in my pockets, clutching coins, keys and lip balm as I watch the evening tumble around me. 'Wannabe' is not just our anthem; it seems to spark eye contact with other female clubbers too. I smile across the shiny, tacky floor, sometimes seeing my old sister's peers, amused by the year 11 takeover. 'Wannabe' is our dancefloor rallying cry and we don't want to let it go. We sing along, only semi-sarcastically, each taking a role. 'Easy V doesn't come for free,' falls to Jenny in her little black dress. We pout and throw our heads back in laughter, a gaggle of tan lines in a cloud of White Musk by The Body Shop. Kim is Ginger, Yorkie and I fight for Sporty, Julie is Posh and Hélène just watches it all, amused, never quite Scary.

Hélène is the person I talk to the most, often to discuss the rest of our friendship circle and their concerning love of crap music and shit TV. We love the chaos of *TFI Friday* and Hélène has a mild crush on Chris Evans. We guffaw at hair carbonara, cooked up by Evans's sidekick Jamie the student, which will later come back to haunt us in a choc-chip cookie. Hélène and I send each other long, hand-written letters in the post that dissect the latest gossip ('our slapper in the sun', is how we unkindly describe a schoolmate, while a tall boy with 'Jarvis trousers' and a jacket in military blue is apparently 'just my type'). Sometimes a Morrissey postcard lands on my doormat and – knowing that my parents will see it first – Hélène fills it only with cryptic teen chat on the reverse. We sign off all our communications with 'Ciao for now, you stupid cow' and sometimes Hélène sticks in random clippings from magazines – an annotated Oasis logo 'to be read backwards' – Shit Is So Apparent In Oasis' Music – and then a Trainspotting cut-out comic strip featuring our hero Rent Boy, aka Ewan McGregor. In one note, Hélène writes to me from a general studies exam, during which she is penning critiques of the other students rather than answering any questions. 'Damn bloody exams,' she writes, explaining that Julie is 'using three gallons of Tipp-Ex every ten minutes', while Liz can 'only just be seen through the smoke coming off her pen'. This letter ends with a teasing line about one of the farm boys: 'John's trousers have a sensual split in them'. On the side of this letter, added later and in red, it says '44% = E'.

*

On week nights, I sometimes sit with Yorkie in the market place, her cassette of *Spice* in the tape slot of her blue Mini. '2 Become 1', 'Say You'll Be There'. The rain beats down on the windscreen, our feet on the dashboard, a bottle of Pepsi rolling in the footwell. Like me, she feels exterior; it's the fate of a tomboy in a provincial town. We both find comfort in the songs, both laughing at them, winding each other up, then finding poignant meaning in the lyrics. Radiohead's 'Thinking About You' breaks us, often, which is why we return to the brassy cartoon world of *Spice*. Yorkie winds down the window to get rid of her ash. She's talking about her band and their upcoming gig at the Harrogate Arms, a slightly intimidating venue full of goths and metalheads. I admire her bravery. I look through the twinkly lights of my cute hometown, hoping to see a different reflection in the Oxfam shop where I found my white Fred Perry.

We sometimes drive out to Brimham Rocks in Yorkie's car to look for aliens on the horizon. We drive in convoy, with our mate Chris, who we all call Moggy, up ahead. The eerie hum of Menwith Hill, a US military listening post, hovers across the fields as we wait, looking for lights in the sky. We constantly shush each other's chat so as not to miss possible communication from extra-terrestrials hiding in North Yorkshire's hedgerows. Moggy brings a rucksack that he calls the 'bag of delights': inside it, a two-litre bottle of Coke, which we all swig, Wagon Wheels and bags of Skips, which we crack out when the alien craft fail to show.

14

Blu Tack wars

In the Cross Keys with Yorkie and Ollie, with Brennan behind us, minutes after blowing my budget on Pernod and lemonade.

I'm in the sixth-form corridor waiting for Craig to deal me an illicit bag of Frazzles. He's bending down at the side of the vending machine, the door temptingly swung open, its bounty reachable. At his feet is a stack of cardboard boxes blocking the cloakroom door and enabling our furtive transaction. Craig, who has sideburns, is one of the boys who only arrived at our school a few months ago for sixth form and is trusted by the head of year to be our tuck shop stock monitor. He refills the vending trays twice a week with crisps, soft drinks, sweets and chocolate bars as we, his inner circle, watch on eagerly and promise not to corrupt the process. He's good at his job and looks after us: we see these infrequent covert exchanges as rightful payback for the times when the machine gets stuck, a Drifter wedged between the silver metal coils, a tube of fruit Toffos teasingly jammed against the glass.

Around the corner, to the left of Craig's sugary kingdom, is the sixth-form common room where a battle for the walls has begun. We have two huge reversible posters, each from *Select* magazine. I side with the Chemical Brothers over Jamiroquai. The Blu Tack is worn, dry and flecked with bits of cream paint, but we work it back to life in our hands and I switch the image over whenever I get the chance. The alternative to Jay Kay's space cowboy outline is the cover of *Exit Planet Dust* with its pale blue sky, American muscle car and roadside couple, who seem exotically but casually in love. This image seems to offer a passageway to a faraway dreamland where palm trees line the highway. I want to be there, and I want to be one of them. The music is better too, which I inform those gathered around the hi-fi on a regular basis.

We sit around on seats that run along the edges of our space in a large lop-sided rectangle. Tall single-pane Victorian windows at our backs cast us in silhouette: legs crossed, knees in dark blue tights, our dumped school bags punctuating repeating rows of limbs. Flat cushions shift about on well-worn wood, revealing bits of foil and gum wrappers from previously concealed contraband. Down the side of my seat, there's a 4B pencil with no lead and a solitary Rizla paper. Despite this being year 12 and the start of our A-levels, at King James's School we are still required to wear uniform and so the boys are in dark grey suits, striped ties and pale blue shirts, while the girls are in white, red and blue Dress Stewart kilts with navy or burgundy jumpers. This studious look is at odds with the grinding beats on the stereo and this enforced smartness undermines our efforts to make this corner of our school kingdom feel like the chill-out room in a club. We can't smoke in here, but some of the boys push a cigarette behind their ears anyway.

*

'The brothers gonna work it out . . .' says the voice at the start of 'Leave Home', and I want to follow it out through the common room door, down the stairs and into a throbbing festival field. I do so in my head, weaving and ducking through packed sweaty bodies towards a circle of dancing feet. I look down and see dusty trainers sweeping in joyful circles, occasionally a wrist-banded festival arm dipping down to drop a cigarette butt into the dry earth. I am blinded by a strobe when I look up, an ascending chainsaw guitar pulling my body into the sky before slamming it back down with a squelchy bassline that tastes of warm lager and the bitter tang of a pill pushed into my hand by a boy in Evisu jeans. A metallic sound, a tiny quiver of Kraftwerk, a trip to the moon via the desert, but first over a farm fence where a girl gets her Gatecrasher t-shirt spattered with the aftermath of a hidden cow pat.

CONNECTION IS A SONG

Somebody's blonde dreadlock hits me in the face as I round a corner with a sign pointing campers back to Gate D. I laugh to myself when the tree turns into a pylon. The main stage is so boring, I tell the hedge. The place to be is this dark, dancing enclave with the perilous but very funny mud patch by the door. A girl trips on a rope and falls flat. We look the other way to save her blushes, thankful it didn't happen to us. A cityscape rushes by on stage as Tom and Ed hunch over their impossibly large keyboards. They are moving just enough to show us they are real, but otherwise they could be cardboard cut-outs in the vague shape of the Chemical Brothers.

Driving space beats zoom me back into the dense middle earth of the crowd and I find myself up in the point of the tent, inside an inverted cone, my face gently pressing against taught clammy nylon, my eyes looking down on the murky throng where my friends are exchanging sweat and spit. I'm high on the rattling sound of the Brothers, on a brain voyage that keeps switching between Scooby Doo chase scenes and the need to control an airship that is floating too close to the sun. I giggle at the responsibility, inhale the smell of warm grass and then land back in the common room, my trainers replaced by black Doc Martens that seem to splash onto the scratchy grey carpet.

In the Chemical Brothers, we find near-unanimous common room approval, a reprieve from endless debates around which *Star Wars* film is the best, a dangerous foray into contemporary politics (there's an unlikely resistance to the rise of New Labour) and whether Oasis will make a bigger impact on music than the Stone Roses. The Chemicals' crunching 2 a.m. sound keeps the teachers away and feels slightly anarchic between history and English, and so my group seizes control of the black Hitachi mini system as well as the walls.

*

Craig is known by his surname – Tetley – and is our low-key chief of staff. Among the other boys, Brennan (also known as Steve) is our leader of comic timing and Gus is our head of cynicism. Banky (Matthew) and Rich (sometimes known as Perky, his surname is Perkins) are here too, waiting for their moment to deliver a wry comment but otherwise quietly observing as the rest of us show off. Hélène, my best friend in the group, is kind and mature, always chuckling and making others feel better about whatever social drama might be unfolding for them. She loves John Peel's radio show and we bond over Pulp's *Different Class*, especially the lyrics to 'Underwear'. Jenny, with the accidental Britpop fringe, is the girl that all the boys fancy, but she wears it lightly and manages to break any tension with a well-timed *Friends* quote. Julie and Kim are trying out being grown-ups, and want to put on TLC, while Yorkie and I clown around doing stupid voices, all the while clocking a deeper understanding of each other's Radiohead-flavoured inner world.

Despite our forceful musical takeover, there's a new kind of democracy in the sixth form. Being smart is no longer a dark secret to hide, boys are friends with girls without a snigger, and we look after each other: sharing our snacks in free periods and covering for each other when questioned by teachers over our whereabouts or frequent lateness. We work hard, which is why it is a surprise when Mrs Turner turns me, Julie and Louise away from a lesson about Henry VIII's domestic policy, on account of us being five minutes late. We go back to the common room and sit in amused disbelief, then we pull out our textbooks and write notes about the Field of the Cloth of Gold anyway.

While this is happening, I look across the room and see Miss Smith, the German teacher I admire; a young woman with a neat brown bob, shuffling through to Mr Hall's office, the head of sixth form. She is clutching a pile of exercise books and looks ever so slightly nervous as she makes her diagonal journey through our territory. I feel a rush of something like sorrow, or perhaps empathy, as I monitor her progress, overloaded and further hampered by our teenaged limbs crisscrossing her path. She glances my way and the funny feeling from Asda returns. I'd like to jump up and offer to take the books from her arms, but I don't. I just watch her and tentatively smile.

*

On the other reversible poster, there is a choice between the Stone Roses – Ian Brown in his famous money t-shirt – and Oasis's Gallagher brothers posing in their sky-blue Manchester City tops, their faces looming into shot, the resolution on their monobrows altogether too sharp. The Blu Tack works hard again and we knead it back into compliance. I vote for the Roses, as usual, and we start our regular argument about which band will one day be deemed the most influential in all of music. I chip in with a vote for the Smiths (the true icons of Manchester indie, you fools), but this peripheral viewpoint falls on deaf ears. I make the case that the Roses connect our current music scene with the rave movement of the late-'80s and that they are part responsible – along with Primal Scream – for the melding of guitar and dance music, which can only be a very good thing. That Oasis 'will play bigger stadiums', 'have more number ones' and 'be famous in America' seems to be the opposing justification. I often buy a music magazine or paper – my new obsession is *Raw*, a kind of *Smash Hits/NME* crossover – on the way to school so that I can lounge around with it in the common room. This detour, every Wednesday, makes me late, but the opinions I glean from the journalists help me fight my poster battles. Oasis might be selling more records, but you should care more about Gorky's Zygotic Mynci. This thought goes the way of the Smiths.

'I Am the Resurrection' blasts across our space at the start of morning break, its insistent beat reaching me at the doorway as I tumble in with my black plastic art folder, which always seems to catch my shins. The sun is streaming in through the windows, the air smells of socks and Dr Pepper. It's Ollie who's put the Roses CD on and I nod my approval as I watch him in his Kappa zip-top chatting up the new girl.

I have a spiralling fish-eye view of the room; my schoolmates gathered in a series of small chattering circles, their Venn diagrams of friendship merging and separating as the tune melds around their conversations. The shy kids cling to the edges, but they are part of this too. My crew, as expected, occupy the seats nearest to the hi-fi. Hélène is in her cream jumper, leaning back and laughing. Brennan is hunched, hands in his pockets, saying something that makes Rich chuckle. Jenny is playing with her fringe and it looks beautiful.

*

'She's chucking a whitey,' groans Gus, pushing his seat away from the table laid out with Star Wars Monopoly round at his house, a double-fronted Victorian villa up by Scriven Green. The boys pretend they know about whisky, while we drink bottles of Hooch and Becks. Gus's parents don't seem to mind the house filling up with drunk teenagers and so we congregate here, listen to his dad's Beatles albums and sometimes do a bong. We're sitting on the rug in the living room when I find myself unexpectedly staring upwards, the ceiling rose spinning in a strange, rotating blur. It's me 'chucking the whitey', whatever that means, which is an inconvenience because I was just about to learn the chords for 'Fake Plastic Trees' with Yorkie. A pint glass of water is shoved into my hand, and I gulp it down. With each cold flush at the back of my throat, I feel awake, but in a strange way. My mouth doesn't feel quite like my mouth, my nose has that swimming pool feeling and the music – now Pink Floyd – is being piped into my head via an icing bag with a star-shaped nozzle. I am a half-iced cake, spongy and sweet. I feel sick. I don't remember how I got here. I dream a dream soundtracked by the Stone Roses' *Second Coming*, which may or may not have really been on in this room, and later I come round on a sofa full of Gus's mum's patchwork cushions, the beads along the edge of one of them pressing into my left temple. I can hear the soft chuckle of the Monopoly game, still going. I shuffle in and reach for the peanuts that I hope will ground me back on earth.

One of these nights there is high drama when the boys decide to dislodge a stone sphere from the gatepost of a posh house on the way back from a pool night in town. They roll it all the way to Gus's while the girls follow behind, drunk too but eye rolling as we observe their quest. Nobody notices the chalk mark being drawn along the pavement, leaving the perfect Miss Marple trail for the local police to follow the next morning. Gus's parents are woken early and the boys, all with hangovers, are dragged out of bed and ordered to roll it back.

15

The blue Mini

It's dark and condensation fogs the windscreen. We're listening to *The Bends* as it crackles in the tape slot of Yorkie's pale blue Mini Cooper, which she calls Barney. This car, with its two white stripes down the bonnet, is like a favourite trainer: its sportiness a relic of a previous era that we don't want to let go, its seats now pre-formed to our awkward shape – my knees under my chin on the passenger seat, Yorkie's right foot crossed over her left thigh, a thick trainer sole nudging the gearstick. We fit into its small dimensions with a sigh, the upholstery swaddling us, the smell of the dashboard – rainy plastic, a damp metallic tang – a familiar comfort. Yorkie has covered the brown plastic seats with blue plaid material, which brushes against my face when I turn to her. Up ahead in the night air, two round light beams pick out the drizzle as we throw the stubs of our Marlboro Lights from the windows. I'm resting my elbow on a cold metal rim that leaves a pleasing straight line down my forearm to my wrist. My watch face glints in the wing mirror, but I don't look at the time. Instead, I am gazing along the edge of the road, watching night-time clouds move slowly inside silver puddles. We spend many nights like this, parked in country lanes, listening to our songs.

We both look too young to go out in Leeds or York, which is why we often end up this way. In Knaresborough, we find our way into the back rooms of pubs to play pool, or watch others play pool, Yorkie's cigarettes forever resting on the edge of the table, an ash tray clunking into her rum and coke or my half lager. We keep losing the little green indented chalk and, being such professionals, we can't possibly play on until it's found and we have re-powdered the tips of our cues like we are live from the Crucible on BBC2. I only hit my stride after three drinks, potting three reds in a row. I know I have peaked.

Radiohead are the band that nobody ever argues against and even the Cross Keys jukebox offers up a couple of their songs. The opening guitars on 'High & Dry' – mournful with a hint of anger – drift across the bar and I slide my cue across the green baize with just a little more violence. It seems to work: a satisfying quiver into the middle pocket, then clunk. As I survey the table for my next shot, my ears catch the lyric about flying on a motorcycle and watching all the ground beneath you drop.

*

I buy the cassette single of 'Just' from Woolworths and it comes in one of those paper slips which hold the tape just snug enough for it not to fall out. On the cover, R-a-d-i-o-h-e-a-d is spelt out in a montage of photographs: fragments of letters from signs and doors, number plates and old fences with peeling paint. This band seems hidden from me in cryptic layers; Thom Yorke doesn't want to be seen and he doesn't care about his fringe. There's a metal padlock on the cover, a dark joke at the expense of the lyric about changing the locks three times. Whatever Yorke's enemy, it can't be shut out and still comes reeling through the door. I don't exactly know what he is singing about, and nor does Yorkie, but we both seem to feel it, in our own ways. 'You do it to yourself,' Thom says. 'And that's what really hurts.' I deduce that it's a song about the helplessness of depression and without needing to say anything at all, I know that Yorkie knows this too.

The distant sound of traffic has always lowered my mood, the very worst poison being a whining motorbike on a faraway street. I can't explain why. The first time I noticed, I was a very young child – no more than eight – looking through the curved bay window in Nanny Olive's bedroom at the front of my grandparents' house on Grove Lane in Headingley in the suburbs of Leeds.

I am standing at her dressing table, wary of the sharp edge of its glass top. Nanny's hairbrush faces upwards, a tangle of white curls, but I know not to touch it or to move any of her things. A box of hairpins shines with a mother-of-pearl lid. The room smells of old curtains and mothballs. The bed is very properly made, a sheet pulled taught across the mattress with a thick pale pink quilt and a blanket laid neatly across the top. I can't imagine the 'mad half-hours' that our mum describes from her childhood – a free-for-all playtime of bouncing mayhem, apparently in this very room with Nanny letting loose and tickling her daughter to infinity among the pillows.

I look outward, beyond the garage opposite where Nanny used to hold me up as a toddler to watch the cars go through giant rollers and come out all soapy on the other side. I look to the blue-grey hillside; a gap in suburbia, a horizon to fix my gaze. And then I hear it, a lonely motorcycle[i] powering along some unknown street, maybe half a mile away. My heart sinks with a sudden desolation and I am surprised by the force of the sensation. I tell no one about it, but it's a feeling that will come to find me again and often through a song. I realise that I can bring on a kind of *contained sadness* at will, and then quell it again when the waves get too strong. *The Bends* is the faraway motorbike, speeding me towards the edge of something, but it's not the obviously sorrowful tunes that hold the power. 'Street Spirit (Fade Out)' is mournful, yes, but it doesn't fully prod my motorcycle nerve. It's the gently descending chords at the start of '(Nice Dream)', the track preceding 'Just', that sweeps me

---

[i] Years later when I first hear the song 'Motorcycle Emptiness' by the Manic Street Preachers, I wonder if my depressive response to this sound is a known phenomenon. Even later, when I ride my own motorbike – albeit a 50cc Vespa with a hairdryer engine – I wonder if my journeys are being heard and felt by a new generation of teenagers mournfully staring from bedroom windows.

back to that moment in Nanny's room, a sepia-flavoured sense that happiness is something only found in the past.

'Just' contains enough fire to shake the melancholia off my back, and I play my cassette single at top volume up in the loft, rewinding the A-side repeatedly so that I can go through it all again. Thom Yorke seems to be fighting the motorcycle mood, a terror that suckers him but not his friends, and I swear that I feel the same, and that Yorkie gets it too. This subliminal sharing of angst all takes place in between jokes about our teachers ('I felt so feminine tonight,' once uttered by a history teacher, becomes a repeat source of mirth) and swigs of Pepsi.

I want to spit out the lyrics just like Thom Yorke – whose saliva I can hear slapping into the microphone – and I want to follow Johnny Greenwood's guitar upwards to its place under the clouds. I'm tracking behind them both in a heady spiral of racing anxiety, my knees scraping across rocks, my hands scrabbling into tiny spaces full of dust, not noticing or caring about the pain in my legs, the grazes down my arms, or the inevitability of tomorrow's scabs, which I will try not to pick, but will do so anyway.

*

Back in the confines of Barney, rainwater dribbles through the gaps we've left in each of the front windows as Yorkie pops open the Marlboro Light packet and points a cigarette in my direction. I smoke one for every three of hers as we edge towards the thing we need to talk about. We turn over *The Bends*, playing for time, and sink into the opening ice winds of 'Planet Telex', shielding ourselves for another few moments from serious talk. We let it wash over us and as I stare into the night, the music seems briefly in sync with the tiny streams of water finding their multitude of routes down the glass, a burgeoning tree of tributaries that eventually glob like tears into the door handle's cavity. *You can force it but it will not come.*

Yorkie and I have a shared secret that we begin to describe to each other in code. We both have a crush on the same person, who we decide to call 'Bernard'. Neither of us knows how this came to be our euphemism, but I'm pretty sure it was Yorkie's idea, knowing that the incongruity of the name will make all future discussions in this area at least funny. As we begin opening our hearts to inner truths, allowing little rivers of thought that we have yet to let flow through ourselves, the name will catch us like a big hairy dog, or a grumpy old man, and we will find ourselves shaking with laughter and spluttering out warm Pepsi at every mention; the more unexpected the better ('I love Bernard's hair', 'Bernard isn't coming out tonight', 'Bernard is not well'). We make sure the code word bounces only between us, and is never overheard, because – of course – the problem for both of us is that Bernard is a girl.

Our friendship group works in concentric circles, with Yorkie and I central to social occasions but often found re-orbiting the perimeter as the night sets in. We find our way back to the middle through in-jokes and, in my case, seizure and control of the kitchen CD player. We are funny enough and confident enough to scale the hierarchies, to dominate games of Shit Head, to stick on the Manic Street Preachers (me) or Garbage (Yorkie), but often we find ourselves fading into the night – and I find myself invisible.

*

THE BLUE MINI

Despite Yorkie's Nirvana mosh pit tendencies and my incurable music snobbery, we both love pop music and often change the Radiohead tape for the Spice Girls or Madonna. We have a nice little growing obsession for a new song by American band, No Doubt, whose track 'Don't Speak' seems to be drenched in the hopeless feelings we both have for Bernard. It's a break-up song, but somehow it seems to signify the end of a time in which we can pretend nothing will ever change. Singer Gwen Stefani is in denial about things falling apart, and she doesn't want to look reality in the eye, as myself and Yorkie are trying to do, through a haze of smoke and a cryptic name. In the middle eight, Stefani briefly finds acceptance – 'we've got to stop pretending who we are' – but the track's pleading, heartbroken quality is what hangs around us on the blue plaid as we decide we should probably join the others in the pub.

*

My first proper job is at Maynews, the newsagents on the corner of Knaresborough market place, and the very good Saturdays are when Yorkie and I are on shift together. We stand side by side in blue tabards, awaiting the good-looking dad who orders in the *Socialist Worker* and always asks for it with a flirty twinkle that doesn't seem very Karl Marx. He tucks it under his toddler in a pushchair, thanks us extremely politely, and skips away past the fishing nets and the tub of plastic footballs by the door, and out onto the cobbles towards his mysterious real life. He is unaware that he is a *known customer*, one that we wait for, and that without his appearance our day is strangely incomplete. Other regulars include the Murray-Mints-and-*Mail* woman, the Navy Cut granny, and numerous men who buy angling magazines with a huge fish on the cover. These are so reliably bought that we don't need to order them in. Of the music press, only *Kerrang* and *Mojo* are dead-cert sales, but I keep buying *Select* – and amassing the free tapes.

Selling cigarettes is our main shop duty with at least one in three customers asking for silver Lambert & Butlers. We become so adept at locating each brand on the shelves behind the counter that, when it's quiet, we play a game in which one of us shouts two cigarette makes, while the other forms the necessary body shape to pick them out without looking. We get caught doing this when the shop door pings open and quickly fold ourselves back into something like normal. We love being abnormal, though, and weep with laughter when one of our combinations calls for a yoga-esque manoeuvre between Silk Cut and Peter Stuyvesant. In summer, we dread anyone asking for an ice cream because penetrating the row of irredeemably rock-solid trays of vanilla, strawberry, rum and raisin, and mint choc chip with a scoop that is not up to the job feels like a strange sort of mountaineering task that is forever beyond us. When I fear an ice-cream order is imminent, I busy myself tidying the subscription rack and drop Yorkie in it, giggling as I crouch low and slowly go through the alphabet, checking several times over that the farming and knitting magazines have arrived.

*

Bernard is on our minds when Euro '96 arrives and – just like Italia '90 – it is clear for all to see that England are going to win. All of us

meet at Kim's house for the England-Netherlands game and agree
that our mix of old hard-nuts (Teddy Sheringham, Tony Adams,
Stuart Pearce) and players who are nearly as young as us (Robbie
Fowler is four years older at twenty-one) will see us lift the trophy.
Brennan is ensconced in the corner with his four-pack of Challenge
lager that we all call 'yellows'. With the match panning out like
a dream (England are on top, England are running riot), Hélène
and I pop to the top shops to buy more wine. When we get to
the counter, the shopkeeper asks which one of us is eighteen. We
panic and each point at the other (we are both still seventeen) like
a farcical *Two Ronnies* sketch but, strangely, he sells us the bottle
anyway. We walk back along Boroughbridge Road in the hot dusty
day back to Kim's and in time to see England triumph 4–1 against
the mighty Dutch. I pinch myself, slug another gulp of sweet white
wine, and send my eleven-year-old self, still with Gazza's tears on
her cheeks, the good news.

Our celebrations get expectedly messy, we play our guitars
in the top room and I exchange Bernard glances with Yorkie
through a descending fog of wine. When my head starts spinning
(the light bulb in the lamp above us won't keep still), I go for a
lie down in the 'brown room', one of the multiple living rooms
in Kim's parents' house. The main lounge, with the big TV –
and with Brennan in the corner sinking yellows – is pink. I don't
know the significance of the colours (other than the décor, which
reminds me of an American home of the 1980s, the ones you see in
films) or whether there's a snooker theme, but I stare at the ceiling
for a while, pondering the way these hues affect the atmosphere
of a place. I think about the days of the week, why Tuesday, to
me, is pale green, and Thursday quite obviously orange. I wonder

why pastels seem to evoke a sense of resignation in me. Perhaps then I sleep, perhaps I scale rum-and-raisin mountains in my dreams. When I become aware of myself again, I have no idea of the time or of how long I've been there. All I know is that I can hear Bernard laughing next door.

16

The drunk crucifer

It is Christmas Eve and I'm about to do my other job, the one
where I wear a white habit, dilute the holy sherry and snuff out
candles. I am a church crucifer, a role given to the oldest of around
twelve teenage volunteers, in part to bear the sheer weight of the

brass crucifix with its heavy wooden stem on its journey down the aisle each Sunday. We in our late teens are deemed both physically strong enough and with the required sense of responsibility for this important task. We are called 'servers' because this is the Church of England, but in this ancient building with its incense-infused transepts, we are performing the centuries-old Catholic duties of altar girls and boys. Claire has gone before me obediently and, as with many things that she does, I must fall in line behind.

Despite my compliance, I feel my heart sink whenever I see my name on the rota, which is pinned behind the heavy door in the vestry near the cupboard with the 400-year-old silver chalices. Sometimes (and we hate this), the vicar calls our home landline to check that we have remembered, presuming – accurately – that teenagers will probably, usually, forget their ecclesiastical obligations. When Claire realises that she is on the list to carry the cross the morning after Pulp's headline set at the Heineken Music Festival in Leeds in 1995, a deep depression passes through the late-night house, followed by a quiet, hungover acquiescence when the morning arrives. I breathe a sigh of relief that it's not me experiencing this level of comedown but after dragging herself to church, she returns happy and says she spent two hours thinking only of Jarvis Cocker striking Jesus poses in his shiny silver shirt. He has the same initials as the Messiah, I realise, and tell Claire.

It is Mum who has signed us up to being church servers and, as much as we roll our eyes, we don't want to let her down. After Claire's Pulp epiphany, I try my best to spend my church time in a pop-video state of mind. I already know that there is a religious feeling to pop fandom so, in my head, I toy with Madonna's rosary beads. It is my own 'Like a Prayer', imagining the cool brown wood clinking around my wrists, a black Jesus dripping waxy tears onto the stone floor at my feet. And then I see the stooping figure of Belle and Sebastian's Stuart Murdoch kneeling to pray after sweeping up shiny little pools of disco dust that have fallen through the stained-glass windows in the Sunday sun.

On this Christmas night, I am leading the choir into midnight mass, which everyone knows is the most exciting service of the year. St John's is a near 1,000-year-old church that teeters on top of Knaresborough's famous Crag close to Waterbag Bank, a steep cobbled street that leads tourists and drunk teenagers down to the river. I think of the generations of worshippers who have walked across the smooth flagstones up to these large wooden doors before me – and none of them spangled by afternoon drinking. This is the most important crucifer job. It is a great honour. I have been chosen because they think I'm sensible.

I am absolutely wasted.

*

Belle and Sebastian are a mysterious Scottish band whose singer is a church caretaker who lives in a flat above a church hall. The band arrive on the pop scene like a freshly inked fanzine in 1996 and Claire gets their debut album *Tigermilk* on tape. We listen together with intrigued devotion and agree that the music makes us feel that it must have existed before, perhaps hidden in a library, recorded in a room that smells of the fake burgundy velvet inside a violin case. We swim in its Polaroid nostalgia, hungry to create our own version of these longed-for yesterdays that might yet happen tomorrow. The songs make us lament the rain that fell on a sports day twenty years ago, our plimsoles threadbare at the toes, our thin pale arms dappled in beads of water. The new-old sound of *Tigermilk* also thrusts us into the Glasgow indie scene that we suspect is happening – without us – right now on Sauchiehall Street in the pale light of a spring afternoon.

The first song on the album is 'The State I Am In', which introduces us to Murdoch's fragile vocal, weaving its way across a sparse acoustic guitar. The song blossoms with chiming, sunny chords and a reference to a happy day in 1975, which seems immediately both funny and sorrowful (just one day of happiness for seven-year-old Stuart). A softly brushed drum then laces a melody that seems always to have been in our heads, echoing from the room above the church. The track is playful despite the melancholia; it is Nick Drake without the overwhelming sadness. As Claire and I listen, we eagerly learn the stories of numerous intriguing characters who make up the world of Belle and Sebastian, threaded together by terry towelling shorts, trips to Marks & Spencer and flute solos. There is a child bride, a gay brother (who has 'confessed') and a crippled friend whose crutches Murdoch kicks, shocking me afresh on each listen (he cures her, allegedly). There is a priest with a photographic memory who takes away Murdoch's sins and writes 'a pocket novel called *The State That I Am In*'. There's a school where 'the boys go with boys and the girls with girls' and someone in Glasgow will know it is them when Murdoch declares 'riding on city buses for a hobby is sad'. I later find myself taking the circular routes in Leeds with New Order on my minidisc player – and they are the saddest little happy hours in my week.

Back in Claire's bedroom, Murdoch is puzzled by a dream that stays with him all day in 1995. Listening, trying to unpick the meaning, we revel in this mysterious nostalgia that is not ours and we delight in being wistful about a year that has only just passed. With its Smithsy artwork (monochrome visions of life inside a kitchen-sink drama; paperback covers that seem to offer their own *Choose Your Own Adventure* backstory), it could not be more up our alley and – as usual – I follow Claire into a new pop meadow that is sprouting with both wildflowers and an unexpected view across the city.

*

As I look forwards, trying not to feel sick, I see the church twinkling in the glow of Christmas lights, which beam from a tall, dark tree in the far corner beyond the trestle tables with their pamphlets about coffee mornings. Its boughs reach to me like graceful arms beckoning a time of reflection on the receding year. Despite my inebriation, I find myself inwardly asking for new experiences in the twelve months about to begin. I am otherwise unable to enjoy the magic of Christmas because I'm fighting my eyes, asking them to focus, and trying to give them something secure to fix upon. I choose the little wooden board up ahead with tonight's hymn numbers carefully propped up in grooves: a Victorian mahogany version of Ace of Base in the Asda chart rack.

My head feels weirdly loose on my neck. Nobody knows that I've been drinking sweet, sickly liqueurs since lunchtime, clinking my glass with reckless abandon across the glass coffee table at Yorkie's house. I've added a pint of lager to the cocktail of stupidity. I have tried to sober up with water, a packet of crisps (Seabrooks, ready salted) and gasps of December air, but time taunts me as the hands on the clock tick dreadfully to midnight without a care for the absolute state that I am in. As usual, we assemble in the vestry and I pull on my white nylon cassock, hoping it will somehow begin to cleanse me as I try to blink myself sober. I make no eye contact with anyone and just nod to say that I am ready to do my job. Choristers, old and young, in frills of white and red, leave by the side door and snake gracefully through the night to the main doorway. I walk in front of them and, despite my predicament, I manage to set an even pace.

Like Stuart Murdoch, I give myself to sin. Nobody must know, and especially not Mum. I am pleased that I do not immediately stumble, finding the steady walk a small comfort. The slapping plod of shoes on gravel helps, a metronomic certainty that I dial myself into. My only wish, as I look up at painted silver angels in the rafters, is that this will all be over soon. We stand and pause in the entrance. I glimpse an orange glow from inside and feel that childish shiver of festive excitement. It is Christmas Eve and I want to savour its special feeling. As we move inside, I look over to the right where Mum usually sits, but the sudden turn of my head brings new problems. A nauseating feeling rises from my stomach as a whoosh of winter hats slides by in a blur. I am not through this. I see Mum's ginger hair and familiar winter scarf as she stands neatly holding tonight's service sheet. Her presence gives me an urgent focus: I really must not fuck this up. For her, I will make it down the aisle. I look ahead and wait for the vicar to indicate for me to start the final ten metres of the procession, up to the altar. I glance to see the ceiling spin as I hear the choir begin 'Once in Royal David's City'. It is beautiful and my spine tingles, despite everything. Breathing deeply, in through my nose, out through my mouth, I walk forwards in a ruinous haze, a sludge of Sheridan's, vanilla and chocolate, glooping through my guts.

*

Gentle bleeps call from another universe, a wailing noise, a lost transistor radio bobbing in the waves of a strange electric-blue sea. Cliff Jones, Gay Dad's singer, is presenting himself as an indie Christ and I'm eager to follow this self-declared rock star – and possible cult leader. I've seen him in crucifix pose on the front of the *NME* and with his stigmata oozing fresh red on the cover of *Select* magazine. He has nice hair and I feel ready to fall in love with a new pop star: all the better if he makes church more interesting.

'To Earth with Love' is the song that is sent to convert the fading Britpop masses. Part Bowie, part Slade, it is farcically grandiose but still very English, like a powdered wig down the chippy. Jones urges us to 'use the latest sciences to make your world a better place' as he invites us inside a 'supernatural fairytale'. This is good, I tell myself, because really I prefer science to religion. It's all done with a rock 'n' roll heaviness that I want to like, but that I am still learning to want. Cliff, with his nice eyes, is speeding me towards a cosmic launchpad where Menswear and Mansun have just done their space training and their sparks are still flying from the thrusters. This time there are no cuff links, but the same unhinged show-off energy. Is this what the men's loos are like in Soho House? A haze of hairspray and squeaking trousers? I turn a blind eye to the singer's leathered legs, but they remain a concern as I grapple with the idea of life beyond the brown corduroys of Britpop.

Jones, gripped by the knowledge of his own imminent and assured superstardom, screeches the song's title – 'To Earth with love!' – while summoning his own kind of glam-galactic spirit. It is hairy, this music, and I'm still not sure. Back at the launchpad, everyone's forgotten to put on their flame-retardant suits. Gay Dad (does their name stand up to 21st-century scrutiny?) appear on the cover of all the main music magazines in quick succession. I am fascinated by the 'saviours of rock', a status bestowed upon them in a panicky flurry by journalists watching a Union Jack-wrapped carcass begin to turn grey. In my heart, I know Gay Dad are the last part of the pantomime, and probably the back end of the horse, but they still make me grin. I buy the CD single, only slightly furtively, from Woolworths on a Saturday morning. The cover shows a faux street sign, a pedestrian crossing icon on royal blue. I follow.

Music is a scaffold and by climbing across its joists, we build connections that lead to new beams, some of them right angular, and some of them exactly where we expect. Dad's imposing record collection intimidates us, but we replicate his towering slabs of vinyl in miniature in our bedrooms. His Serge Gainsbourg CDs travel mysteriously to other parts of the house. His Shirelles record takes a holiday to the loft. My CDs and cassettes multiply, outgrowing both their shoebox and my newly added Cadbury's Crème Egg tray. It feels Britpoppy to store my music in confectionery trays, which I borrow from Maynews. Claire's tapes reach up the wall in unsteady columns, tottering beside her black ghetto blaster, with Prince at their base, Tindersticks and David Devant in the upper levels.

Back in church, my granny's harmonies are in my head. She takes the low notes, like a humble garden bird, and I want to do the same. Her gentle undertones make the high notes reach higher. On this

cold, dizzy Christmas Eve, I think of her understated, supportive vocal and the thought steadies me. Somehow, and possibly through divine intervention, I lead the choir all the way up to the stalls without the crucifix clattering sideways into a pew. It sways but I correct myself, a woozy ship that finally – thank God! – finds harbour. My final task is to place it in a brass-lined hole at the front of the altar. I take it very, very slowly, watching its descent with grave concentration. I sigh inwardly as it clunks reassuringly into an ancient groove.

17

Inside a marble

I am devouring music and backtracking to find songs and bands that I have missed or not yet known. This, I realise, could go on for some time. A free tape on the cover of *Select* leads me to Mazzy Star, a name that sounds like a meteor shower. I scramble for information and learn that the singer is called Hope Sandoval, which I imagine to be a turreted palace in a distant region of Narnia. It all seems impossibly remote and beautiful, and I visualise a place where snow-capped mountains meet silky purple skies. A campfire glows in the foreground, a wolf slinks by.

I am picturing this landscape as I play 'Fade into You' on my cassette deck while working on a piece for my A-level art project. It's a pen-and-ink drawing of a baby in the womb, inspired by Leonardo da Vinci, and I'm using a drinking straw to blow red, orange and now purple streaks across the paper in little inky rivulets. Mrs Noakes, my art teacher, taught me the technique on one of the big wooden battle-scarred tables in the art block and now I'm risking the pale green carpet in my room by trying it at home. Hélène says 'no one else would think of it' when she looks at my half-finished work, squinting and angling her head. She writes me one of her notes, comparing my creation to the 'chuffing year 10 "I love Oasis" self

portraits' that line our school corrridors. 'Show a bit of originality,' she writes, 'like a baby blowing up, perchance?' I have this note on my desk, a slight breeze making it crinkle under the gap in the loft window. It makes me laugh again as I add it to my ironic Love Hearts box, which is filling up with teenage communications. When I reply to Hélène, I'll suggest giving the exploding baby a dense Gallagher monobrow.

Sandoval's husky, intoxicating vowels come at me with a Californian drawl ('Fadeee-an to you') that sound as far away from North Yorkshire as it is possible to go. 'Fade into you' – what does it mean? Whose is the 'stranger's light' that comes on slowly? I watch the horizon change colour from my window and search for connections along the forest tracks that diverge and re-converge in my head. A fuzz of midnight chords, a melody picked out by moonlit piano, and that voice: *I wanna hold the hand inside you.* The song seems both emotional and geographic, and it occurs to me that this is common to all the music that I love. There is a sense of travel, of driving through darkness in search of a feeling that is somewhere in the criss-crossing branches of ancient trees and fresh green baby leaves. Someone is fading in the shadows, they are visible again, but only briefly and then they are gone. The song is a poem that I keep re-reading and each time I find new meaning. The song is also a central piece in a bigger musical puzzle.

There are obvious roots to follow: I read that Sandoval has toured with Sonic Youth, whose fuzzy guitar chords connect me back to bands I half-know like My Bloody Valentine. I rifle through my dad's records and find my way to the heartbreak of Nick Drake. 'Way to Blue' gives me the same shivers ('Can you understand the light among the trees?') as 'Fade into You', and

I bask in a luxuriously soft, and safe, misery of my own making. Radiohead's *Pablo Honey* brings similar self-induced emotional ruination ('Thinking About You', 'Stop Whispering') and, like Mazzy Star, I find that the loneliness creeps up on you, disguised by the warmth of an acoustic guitar. I am, of course, very much open to this sort of ambush. Jeff Buckley's *Grace* barely apologises for luring me into a state of constant and feverish poetry writing. Words tumble unexpectedly. I blow spatters of ink across the paper while I dream up the next line. I talk to myself about Bernard and then I hide what I've written in the Love Hearts in-tray.

*

We are round at Julie's house on the Eastfield estate, our trainers neatly lined up by the door: Moggy's Nike Air Rifts with their weird hoofy toes, Jenny's pale blue Gazelles, Perkie's white Adidas shell toes, my blue Trimm Trabbs and Yorkie's fat Vans with their skateboard scuff marks along white edges. Banky takes off his brand-new Caterpillar boots with black and yellow laces and we all take a moment to admire them and their hybrid building site/ hip hop style. It's Julie's house, so her shoes – loafers – are tucked away in the understairs cupboard. Socks out, we lounge across the sofas, one of us sporadically going out to the patio for a cigarette, or getting more cranberry juice to sustain our depleting supply of vodka. Moggy pops up to the garage and we switch to bottles of Sol, then Julie's little sister appears at the door in her dressing gown. She is slightly startled by the mass of drunken sixth-form bodies weaving around her living room, so she says a nervous hi and goes back to her chemistry homework.

INSIDE A MARBLE

We are all obsessed by *Romeo + Juliet*, the Baz Luhrmann version of Shakespeare's most famous tale, and as the film unfurls on VHS, we quote the lines to each other with increasing volume. We swoon at Leonardo DiCaprio in his bloodstained Hawaiian shirt during the beach fight scene. We want to kiss Claire Danes, or at least be her. We cry together each time the story ends, but mostly we sing along to the glorious soundtrack on Julie's mum's CD player. There's the hilarious drag queen chaos of 'Young Hearts Run Free', the joyful Scandi-cuteness of 'Lovefool' by the Cardigans and the emotionally overwhelming 'Kissing You' by Des'ree, during which we avoid eye contact for fear of plunging ourselves into embarrassing teary-eyed turmoil. There are little romances springing up among us and around us, and within us, but there's something precious about the group that we also want to preserve.

The songs connect us to the film, but they also put us into our own film, with developing side stories and plot twists involving young farmers and more vodka. Naturally, I don't miss the opportunity to be a music nerd and so I am at pains to tell everyone that 'You and Me Song' by the Wannadies has actually been around for *ages* (I've got the cassette single to prove it, from two years ago, I repeat). And then there's Radiohead's ode to grief, 'Exit Music (For a Film)', but then that's mine and Yorkie's turf and the corresponding sense of desolation shall be reserved for chats in the blue Mini.

*

If it is possible for a song to sound like the inside of a beautiful glass marble, then this is it. We hear Stina Nordenstam's 'Little

Star' in the background following Mercutio's death, during Juliet's 'Come, gentle night' monologue and while its sweet sorrow rivals the melancholia of Radiohead, it is also a salve amid the bullets and gothic neon, its undemanding beauty a source of respite as the story accelerates towards unavoidable sorrow. But away from the movie, and back inside the song, something else has happened. There's a fire at a warehouse. 'You must have wanted the world to know,' sings Nordenstam. Has someone died? Has a comet fallen to earth? I'm listening to the track in my room, looking out across an orange twilight sky, and it's giving me a sensation of small-scale wonder – a child-like belief that another tiny world might exist, and a desire to dive into its wavy, visible yet unreachable translucence.

I have already privately fallen in love with this track, long ago. Shakespeare's most well-trodden tale, lit up MTV-style with its neon crosses, only renews my affection, and I try to claim the track as *my song*, only recently gifted to the wider world, and my friends, via Leo's floppy hair and the box office. But then *that* saxophone solo kicks in, I give myself up to a sensation of tumbling beauty and then feel stupid for attempting to make it my own. I reach for a salt-and-vinegar twirl and realise that it makes me very happy to share these songs.

'Little Star' and Nordenstam's introspection often lands her on lists of the 'saddest music ever', but there's nothing bleak in the serene atmosphere she creates. There's a mood of English singer-songwriter Virginia Astley in the delicate piano, the hazy sounds of the countryside and the occasional church bells. Like Astley, Nordenstam's mournfulness simultaneously paints a pastoral euphoria, and in these aural dreamscapes and long-ago afternoons, I discover a strange ecstasy. There's an echo too of the burbling riverbanks of the Cocteau Twins: an understanding that things don't have to make sense and that nature is always in charge anyway. Listen with your full attention and it feels like swimming in pure, clear water with the possibility of tiny fish tickling your toes.

*

We go out on our skateboards in an attempt to push back the call of revision and the unwanted expectation of maturity. My board has a drunken cartoon dragon on its underside and I'm proud to tell everyone I ride 'goofy foot' (left foot at the back) while also being much too scared to attempt anything that might actually break my bones. Yorkie is far braver than me and tries to grind down the railings in the car park at the arse end of Knaresborough. She succeeds some of the time, but we wince in unison when her elbows come smacking down onto the tarmac. Yorkie wears her wallet dangling on a chain, a cigarette hanging from her mouth, and she knows how to ollie. She keeps on practising while me and the others sit on the kerb drinking from warm plastic bottles – Coke, Tango and Sprite, when what we really want is cider. Moggy leaves his car door open while 'Virtual Insanity' plays from the stereo, and I smile at him while also rolling my eyes. He grins back and says, 'Would you like to come and see my puppies?' He's doing the pretend scary man voice, mimicking the stranger-danger public information films that they still play to us in assembly even though we are seventeen and believe ourselves to be wise. We are expected to live in a permanent state of fear in case we accidentally take ecstasy while crossing a railway with a stranger who wants to get us in his car and drive us to his weird home to see his six non-existent baby Labradors. The puppy man is one of our running jokes and at least Moggy's impression stops me from launching into a diatribe about how he should widen his music taste beyond Jamiroquai.

Beneath the giggles, we are positioning ourselves for a future in which we know we will soon be apart. Hélène, who never goes near a skateboard, is the friend I talk to about these things, usually on the way to someone else's house in her Citroen AX Jazz, which provides us safe passage from Jay Kay with a Pulp soundtrack permanently in the cassette deck. We sing the words out loud to 'Underwear' and 'F.E.E.L.I.N.G C.A.L.L.E.D L.O.V.E' as we career down the high street, windows down, low-key analysing the burgeoning relationships around us. One of our friends has just lost her virginity and proudly claims it happened while CeCe Peniston's 'Finally' ('Finally it has happened to me right in front of my face . . .') was playing portentously on the radio. One day, we are busy chatting about who's kissed who, cruising past the statue of Queen Victoria in the middle of Harrogate, when the Citroen crunches into another car at the lights. Frozen in the passenger seat, it takes me a few seconds to realise what has happened as the door caves in across my knees. Hélène slams on the brakes and our eyes meet in wordless shock. As I pick out little shards of glass from my ear, I realise that Jarvis is still singing.

18

All-nighter with Mum

It's like New Year's Eve in our house, except it is early summer and a gentle whiff of pink blossom wafts through the back door. Mum is in an unusually mischievous mood when I get back from school. She comes to the door in her apron, with a bounce in her step. This Thursday feels different from all previous Thursdays. There's a little bit of tension in the air, like the hours before a wedding or some other formal occasion. Mum has been out flyering, a final push. A roll of red stickers rests on the dresser and I eye them surreptitiously. Later, they will form a piece of family folklore. Behind Mum, on the small wooden kitchen table, are mushroom vol au vents, little rounds of garlic bread, bowls of salad, a large quiche and an apple cake. Wine glasses stand obediently in a row, as if waiting to dance. Dad will come home with a wedge of newspapers and we will all take a last ceremonial look at the opinion polls, which Dad says not to trust. Labour are miles ahead, but the angst of 1992 still looms large, at least for Mum. As dusk arrives, she is adding the final touches to her plans for a general election all-nighter. It is 1 May 1997, and the stickers say 'New Labour, New Britain'.

I skip up two flights of stairs to my room and put on the radio. R Kelly's 'I Believe I Can Fly' is playing, which I hate, so I switch to

Radio 4 and listen instead to news of Prime Minister John Major casting his vote in Huntingdon and his opponent Tony Blair doing the same in his constituency of Sedgefield, followed by a much bigger crowd. The reporter is out of breath and describing record turnouts at polling stations, with just a few hours to go. I ask Mum what time we will be voting, at Knaresborough House at the bottom of the high street, and she says 'soon' with a grin. I am eighteen and this will be the first time I've had any sort of say in an election, let alone this one, which even schoolmates who say they don't care about politics are talking about. I am excited and plan to vote tactically, as I've been advised to do by people who know, because Labour never win in Harrogate and Knaresborough. The area, with its farmers and traditions, is 'true blue', says Mum. I'm reminded of her friend, the councillor, who says she'd vote for a pig in a blue rosette.

*

Jyoti Prakash Mishra – aka White Town – has made a pop song that will not leave my head. 'I could never be your woman,' he sings, confusingly, throughout the first few months of 1997. The track's rolling, rumbling beat is so deeply playful that it feels rude to resist its charms. I'm not the only one who feels this way and the track gets to UK number one for a week before being dislodged by Blur. I write 'Beetlebum' with my finger in the condensation on the window of the blue Mini, and the letters re-appear repeatedly across the next few weeks, annoying Yorkie, but it's White Town's addictive one-hit wonder 'Your Woman' that lives between my ears as the year opens up its petals like a dot matrix image of a rose. I buy the CD EP from Woolworths, its cover featuring green text on a white background and faux computer code that reads '>Abort, Retry, Fail?_'. The artist behind the tune seems elusive, a bit like the new thing being spoken about: the internet.[i] Inside the CD inlay it says 'recorded on analogue 8-track'. A male vocal, sung from the perspective of a woman, beams into 1997 through what sounds like a supermarket Tannoy system, deliberately distant and distorted with occasional bleeps shoplifted from a Commodore 64. It is a strange kind of sister to Babylon Zoo's 'Spaceman', from a year earlier, and comes with a convoluted message about sexual freedom. I learn more in the pop-up captions on the *Chart Show*. The singer says the song might be about 'being a straight guy in love with a lesbian' or 'being a gay guy in love with a straight man' or 'being a straight girl in love with a lying, two-timing, fake-arse Marxist'. I revel in the song's lyrical Twister-like moves and use it to guard myself against the dangerous sixth-form drift towards nights in the Slug and Lettuce with the Gareths of Harrogate. These lads are still hunting us in packs, shrouded only by a cloud of aftershave, and I am still more interested in their trainers than their chat-up lines.

*

I'm meant to be revising for my A-levels,[ii] but Mum's buffet and the BBC's election night programme is too much of a temptation,

---

[i] In the autumn of the year, my friend Hélène sends me letters from her new university digs in Preston. In one, she writes 'If you get the chance to use the Internet (with a very capital "I") my E-mail address is . . .' (she proceeds to fill her name with dots, which I fear would have caused me problems). Back at home, working in Threshers, waiting for my life to start, there is little to no chance of me discovering that this address will fail.

[ii] I develop a way of memorising Shakespeare quotes by saying them out loud set to guitar chords. I find Cast songs 'Alright' and 'Sandstorm' work the best because they are so simple.

so I've come downstairs again to see what's going on. I'm in the living room, crouched on my knees next to the TV, pleased with myself after voting for the first time and still intrigued by the little stubby pencil on a string, the hushed drama of the polling station and the clipboard-wielding seriousness of the volunteers ensuring democracy is carried out to the letter. Mum has invited friends inside for nibbles and drinks, and their presence in our house is adding to the sense of occasion. As the clock ticks towards 10 p.m., when results will start being announced, there's a little wave of anxiety and the chatter in the room falls silent. Mum keeps referring to Neil Kinnock's head in a lightbulb (the *Sun*'s 1992 election day attack on the former Labour leader, and a day later 'It's the *Sun* wot won it' brag) and the disappointment of five years ago, but when David Dimbleby appears in front of six screens – live pictures from the main leaders' constituencies, Huntingdon, Sedgefield and Yeovil, plus Sunderland (famed for being first to announce its results), London's Piccadilly Circus and Big Ben – Mum shoots me a look that is full of hope. Five minutes into the show, we get the first indication of what lies ahead via the BBC's main exit poll. 'Landslide likely' says the graphic, beside an animated red Labour rose and a picture of Tony Blair. We look at each other with wariness and start on the snacks.

The night tumbles onwards like a strange dream, Mum pouring wine and calling in my dad from the kitchen. As he shuffles into the room, a tea towel over his arm, Dimbleby reports that 'safe Tory' Finchley, the former constituency of Mrs Thatcher, has been won by Labour with a fifteen per cent swing. Dad raises an eyebrow and smiles as he goes back to put the kettle on. As things like this keep happening, a mood of quiet disbelief falls upon the room, a 'nobody move' situation. Mum offers round the vol au vents to shake us back to reality. Claire and I destroy a bowl of McCoys crisps without taking our eyes away from the screen, with its constantly rolling ticker of results. We can't get enough snacks; our nerves and excitement seem to demand salt.

The next time I look at the clock it is 3.10 a.m. and Mum is yelping 'Portillo!'. The Tory minister – seen as the likely next Conservative leader – is about to lose his seat in Enfield; Dimbleby says, if the rumours are true, he has 'blown it'. Mum says that history is changing every few minutes and that 'you girls will remember this when you are old'. At the declaration in Enfield, Labour's Stephen Twigg turns his surprised eyes up to the ceiling and grins boyishly as his victory is confirmed, with a shift since the last election of nearly eighteen per cent. Under his breath, Dad mumbles, 'Well, bloody hell'. Each new announcement brings a different kind of gasp. The BBC presenting team seem to be doubting the autocue as they reel off new statistics: Labour has secured the biggest majority since World War Two and it's the lowest share of the vote for the Conservatives since 1832. Any thoughts of going to bed have long been called off. We are all still up for Portillo and well beyond. Only my little sister Kerstin sleeps.

*

'Brimful of Asha' might be described as a classic '90s one-hit won-der alongside 'Your Woman' and 'Spaceman', but Cornershop are in the *NME* every week, so in my head they are a 'proper' band – and anyway I like Tjinder Singh's hair. The singer has a sharp asymmetric fringe and his band seem to have achieved being part of Britpop without needing to smash you in the face with a pointy boot. They are a guitar group with songs about Ford Cortinas and corduroy trousers, but the tracks come with low-slung dance beats and sitars too. Their music, like their name, delivers a tongue-in-cheek take on British-Indian culture (one of their EPs is released on 'curry-coloured vinyl') that holds a mirror up to everyday prejudice while simultaneously giving you a nice big cuddle and a generous puff on the circulating spliff. 'Sleep on the Left Side' features Labour councillors (Singh's dad was a local politician in Wolverhampton) and Sikh traditions (the importance of keeping the sword hand free). But it's 'Brimful of Asha' that blasts the sound of Cornershop into the mainstream and gives the boys in Oasis cagoules a shove. The song arrives on the radio in the summer of 1997 and first gets attention through the lyric, 'everybody needs a bosom for a pillow', which sets off audible sniggering among every man and boy on the land mass of the UK.

While the boob line is sung around school and aimed at us girls, the song hits me with a cryptic rush and a desire to decipher the track's true meaning. I learn about the legend of Asha Bhosle, the Indian singer and 'sadi rani' (Punjabi for 'our Queen') who is the most recorded artist in history, featuring on many thousands of Indian movie soundtracks. Singh says he wanted to write a song about the films that lit up his childhood as an Asian boy growing up in the Midlands, and you can hear the sense of speeding joy in his appreciation of tunes that 'illuminate the main streets and the cinema aisles'.

The album the song comes from – *When I Was Born for the 7th Time* – is released a month later in September 1997. It is birthed into a world of grief-mania as Britain digests the death of Princess Diana, but somehow it brings with it a sunny sense of multicultural optimism, skipping between guitar indie, hip hop and country.

ALL-NIGHTER WITH MUM

The sped-up remix of the track, by Norman Cook, later fires it into towny clubland and I grin when I hear it in Jimmy's, pulling me with its joyful bounce across a shiny floor splashed with somebody else's Malibu and coke.

*

Claire and I have left the house covertly in the pink morning glow of a new day. It is just approaching 5 a.m. and the cool dawn air lands on our cheeks deliciously, like the feeling of a deep thirst being quenched. We also have slight hangovers developing, thanks to Mum cracking out the Martini after midnight and not noticing us pouring extra little drinks for ourselves. The onset of drunken dehydration makes us even more breathless as we head out on our mission. We exit the back gate without making a noise and walk fast up Whiteley Yard to the high street, taking small steps as if to minimise the chance of being seen. We are giddy with a plan that we know is a tiny bit, well, wrong.

The shop fronts look different on this early May Friday, as if twinkling in the first light of a new part of our lives. Claire is grown-up already, but I'm still finding my feet. The street looks cleaner, somehow, but it's the same route that I take to school every day – rushing past Threshers off licence, a glimpse of cobbles as I turn left to look for Lisa, the measuring of progress by Woolworths and the fishing tackle shop, the certainty that if I'm at the Tory Club by 8.40 a.m., I'll be on time. This morning, though, I don't hurry by in a blur. Claire and I stop in the doorway and take stock. We check all around us, furtively, and then pull out two rolls of stickers, one each, from Claire's bag. Little black and red triangles, hundreds of them. We look again down the high street in case of a morning dog walker or any pork-electing councillors, but the day is still and quiet and ours, so we set to work.

The club, a grand Georgian building, has tall sash windows, each with its lintel painted blue. Glancing across the street constantly, we begin our work methodically in tidy rows but soon enough adopt a scattergun technique to get the job done as fast as we can. We can't quite reach the top, so Claire gives me a foot-up and I deftly apply more stickers across the top third of the window, slap-slap-slap, not a minute to spare. I'm giggling now and asking Claire to let me down. She looks up and laughs. We cover the front of the building in this way before standing back to admire our handiwork: the bluest of blue Conservative Clubs mottled in red Labour stickers. We add so many we think it must have turned dark inside, despite the arrival of bright morning sun. We finish the roll by adding stickers to the door handles, before scarpering at speed through the back streets, past the black-fronted, old-beamed building where we used to buy penny sweets, beyond the vets and round the secret way home, by Castle Junior School.

We are gasping for air as we run, glad to be away, and shocked by our own act of mischief. We get back and return to the living room where Mum is rubbing her eyes, but still marvelling at Peter Snow's swing-o-meter. 'It's coming off its hinge,' she chuckles. Dimbleby is back and describing 'a Labour victory of a gargantuan scale'. Mum doesn't realise we've been out and says I ought to get some sleep before school. I say 'There's no point now', but head to my room and lie on top of my duvet anyway, smiling at the ceiling and letting cool air waft across my body from the window.

A couple of hours later, I'm back in my uniform. Tony Blair and Labour have won with a sweeping victory, and I want to know what my classmates think of it all. I walk nonchalantly up the high street, but as I reach the crossroads my heart begins to bump about in my chest. I am fearing some sort of citizen's arrest, or perhaps there is a police car parked with its blue lights flashing, awaiting a girl of my description. Up ahead, though, I see nothing. I squint to see the stickers on glass that glints in the 8.30 a.m. sun. But I can't see them. I wait for the cars to pass and cross by the flower beds and the little bench where we used to sit with bags of cola bottles after school. Still nothing. I can't see them. I cross the road at last and see that every single one – there were hundreds of them – is gone. In a little over two hours, they have been scrubbed clean. As I arrive at school, a sleep-deprived vandal, I try my best to seem normal.

*

Mum and I have another late-night ritual that takes us to far-away bedrooms in south London and to the lives of six law graduates trying to make their way in the big city. We've got ourselves hooked on *This Life* and we watch together covertly on Wednesdays after *Newsnight* on BBC Two. I make a fresh pot of tea as Jeremy Paxman begins his weary conclusion, timing my manoeuvre so as to be back on the settee to hear the announcer introduce this week's episode. Mum and I are excited as the theme tune kicks in and we exchange a look of relief when Dad shuts the living room door, glad that he is oblivious to our habit as he clinks plates in the kitchen and hums to Radio 3. This week, Anna and Miles are off again in their on-off relationship, which means Anna is in one of her deliciously unhinged moods as she tries to hold it together as a permanently hungover barrister.

I am surprised by Mum's enthusiasm for the relentless drink, drugs and sex on display, but I'm not complaining. It feels like a discreet graduation, our weekly routine, and it marks a significant relaxation of house rules since she banned us from watching *Grange Hill* on account of its edgy storylines. I think Mum has a small crush on Ferdy, played by Ramon Tikaram, a handsome leather-clad biker who doesn't say much; he doesn't have to when he lets down his long, luscious hair. Mum doesn't seem to notice or mind that the character is gay. I am delighted when I spot that Anna has the poster for Pulp's 'Common People' on her bedroom wall. I think I want to become her. Or meet her. I can't decide, but I wish she would give up on Miles.

19

Loo roll for Diana

My ridiculous kids' clock, with its yellow Children's BBC logo, blinks me into Sunday morning. Dad got it for me on a trip to London and even though I am far too old for children's TV, I like to think of it as an ironic feature of my teenage bedroom, alongside my Teletubbies door sign and the toys still stuffed in the eaves, an abandoned game of Battleships that we didn't know was the last ever, and a Boggle box with its smooth dice pieces, one of them missing like a wobbled-away tooth. It's much too early for staring at clocks, though, and I sigh to myself as I roll over, the duvet twisting between my legs. I pretend it's not happening, hiding from time as usual, but I know I must heave my body into the day. My shift at Maynews begins an hour from now at 8 a.m. It's my job to drag in the weekend newspapers from the delivery van, so it's important I am on time to stop them from being soaked in late summer rain. Once inside, I will fill them with their glossy innards: a comic strip of celebrity bikinis, dieting solutions and recipes involving crème fraîche, the '90s' favourite ingredient. These supplements present a frieze of the things we are all meant to want. But I am seventeen and I just want to stay in bed.

Without looking, I slide my arm across the smooth orangey varnish of my bedside table and feel my way to the buttons on my Sony radio-cassette player. I turn on Radio 1 and sink back into my pillow. I stay there, trying to swim through the last ripples of sleep, hoping the time is a dream and wondering where Will Smith and Chumbawamba are today. Breakfast radio is meant to be so annoying it gets you up, but this morning all I hear is a bleepy ambient wash. I check the time again. 7.10 a.m. This is very weird. These slow-motion tunes belong in the comedown room of a drum 'n' bass club in the shadows of a rave. I listen hard and I think it might be an obscure track by The Orb, but there are no lyrics to help decrypt the situation, just a strange downbeat wilderness. I jolt myself upright and reach for my clothes: my brown boot-cut corduroys and my £1.20 Fred Perry, over which I must wear a blue Maynews tabard with a popper at the waist.

The low-key songs continue as I pull on my socks and reach for my dark-green Converse One Stars. There are more tracks that seem to shift around and fill space, some occasional sounds of the sea and synth chords that only ever descend. It is an odd ocean to be floating through as I try to be awake. There are no jingles and there is no breakfast show host to explain what's going on. I shrug and pull my face around in the mirror to check for blackheads. I reach for my make-up bag, which is dusty with broken eyeshadow, and pull out my mascara. I've just finished my three-minute beauty routine when everything changes. The radio goes quiet, a deliberate pause becomes an unusual, prolonged silence. And then a very serious Bruno Brookes says he has a special announcement. Just as he begins to speak, Claire comes flying up the stairs to the loft and shouts, breathlessly: 'Have you heard? It's Princess Diana. She's been in a car crash in Paris.'

*

I am falling through space with only the Verve's borrowed string section to catch me. Each violin peak flings me back into the air and it feels like the jolt of gravity versus the violent expansion of a parachute. My neck aches, I'm scared my elbows will hit the trees and I begin to feel that I might accidentally smack my head on the moon.

'Bitter Sweet Symphony' is the epic anthem of summer 1997, its mood of defiant sorrow already in the nation's ears long before the surround-sound grief of late August. The Verve's album, *Urban Hymns*, seems to deliver the first vaccination against the arrogance of Britpop, singer Richard Ashcroft's brow furrowed with end-of-the-century anguish and the tracks all loaded with serious warnings. Yes, there's love if you want it. But stay off the drugs.

As Ashcroft strides down the street in the video, a re-run of the one-take walk of Massive Attack's 'Unfinished Sympathy' but with added violence, he describes a decade that has carved a path of self-destruction: 'I need to hear some sounds that recognise the pain in me.' Staring ahead, the band's rake-like frontman appears possessed as he passes roadworks and a fried chicken shop, eyes wild as he maintains his shoulder-barging momentum. In his single mindedness, the singer shoves past men and women walking the other way. Their protests leave him cold; he doesn't care. In the newsagent in the corner of the market place, it is also dawning on me that the future needs to be forced into being. I need to bump my shoulders.

Before this song, which towers over the summer holidays like a great gothic cathedral, the Verve's lead singer had already captured my attention with his chiselled face and ultimate mod haircut.[i] The Verve seem to be the band that Oasis have most tried to emulate (not the Beatles, as they would have you think) and in Ashcroft's earnest songs about life and loss, I find myself able to like him far more than the Gallaghers with their Union Jack carnations. The Verve do not need to sip prosecco in Downing Street to know they have created the soundtrack of the year. Ashcroft walks down my street and your street in a black leather jacket, making himself unpopular, because the decade is about to smash us into a wall. By midsummer, and through repeat plays of the track on TV and the radio, 'Bitter Sweet Symphony' has taken all of us down the only road we've ever been down, but the side streets threaten heartbreak. 'I can't change, I can't change,' Ashcroft repeats with a wiry conviction. I already want to say the same words, but I don't know why.

*

It is a big morning in the world of news. I walk up the high street, turn right at Greaves', the rival newsagent, and head diagonally across the market cobbles to the front of the shop. I can already see piles of *The Sunday Times, News of the World,* the *Sunday Mirror,* the *Observer,* the *Sunday Express* and the *Mail on Sunday* waiting for me in their tightly twined bundles. It's my job to cut them free, sort them into piles and

---

[i] A few years later, when I'm in my first job at 97.2 Stray FM, I am teased for having 'Ashcroft hair'. It becomes an on-air joke, with even our breakfast show listeners demanding evidence. It's not the first time and it won't be the last time I am compared to a boy.

insert the relevant magazines. It's then my task to sell them, mostly to old ladies who also buy sweets and cigarettes, some of whom wait at the door watching my frantic work through the window, willing me to open up. As I push the supplements into the folds of the papers (the *Mail* is the most annoying to do at speed – it's too thick and the magazine pages stick together with inky static), I see pictures of Princess Diana and Dodi Fayed looking happy together on holiday. I see Diana on a yacht, Diana in a bikini, I see the couple holding hands on a beach. The mood of real life is grim, though, and it feels wrong to be looking at the pair in this way, peering at them through time; another time that is only really yesterday.

My boss Liz is taking a call in the shop's dusty back room. When she emerges, the '90s move into their final act. 'Get all the papers in,' she says, briskly. 'What, everything?' I reply. Yes. As quick as you can, to the back. The second editions are coming.' Liz then locks the front door. Customers squash their noses against the glass, but we pretend not to see them as we scurry around, sweeping our arms around newspaper piles. I'm on my knees grabbing bundles, trying to hold them flat and steady, lifting them like slabs, up and out, ready for them to be disappeared. Somebody bangs on the door. We ignore them. We're panting and heaving, leaflets and cookery segments are flopping out onto the kids' magazine section, a summer sex guide slapping onto the *Beano*, but we let them fall and keep going. We are chucking the papers through the staff door now; no need for tidiness, just speed. Around five minutes later, our work is done and the newspaper shelf stands empty; scratched Perspex, a mouth with no teeth.

We open up again and explain to customers that they must wait a little longer today, that emergency second editions are on their way with fuller details of Princess Diana's death. We repeat this message over the next forty minutes before, finally, the Ackrill van screeches to a halt outside the shop and I begin my untwining duties again, only this time with Sunday papers that are thin and flimsy, each one no more than four folded sheets. 'DIANA DEAD' shout both the *Sunday Mirror* and *News of the World*. 'Diana is dead,' proclaims the *Sunday Express*. 'Princess Diana and Dodi are killed in Paris car crash,' says the *Sunday Telegraph* more sedately. I'm told not to let customers buy any part of the first editions.

Regulars potter through the door, asking for the supplements, but all the magazines, with their pictures of Diana and Dodi in the sun, are ushered from the shop's back door into the van and away into darkness and the pulping machine and to history.

*

We've just passed our A-levels and each of us is waiting to walk down a new path, a criss-cross of destinations that we know in our hearts will take us apart, probably forever. My route is covered in autumn leaves and will wind its way slowly, eventually, to Leeds. Jenny will go to Glasgow, Hélène to Preston, Julie to Leicester. The blue Mini is still parked on the kerb and will remain a haven until Yorkie heads for Newcastle. For now, we are sitting together along a sofa that runs around the edges of a large open-plan room, all eyes on the TV. It is September 1997, and we are on a pre-university goodbye tour to Center Parcs at Sherwood Forest in Nottingham.

We are here to swim and to slide and to do the rap from *Men in Black* incessantly (even I join in, on music snob holiday) and to throw bowling balls while drunk. Moggy arrives in his own car with its Jamiroquai bumper sticker and seems more grown-up than the rest of us as he twirls his car keys around a finger. We smuggle in two of the other boys – Martin and Gus – in order to get them into our chalet on the cheap. Stealth-like, we drop them off one by one outside the perimeter wall. They each wait in a bush at the side of the road until we return to pick them up and stow them in the boot of Julie's mum's car. To all our surprise, it works and they stay for the whole trip in sleeping bags on the sofa where we are sitting now. This strange holiday feels like a flume between worlds. Also on our schedule: Princess Diana's funeral.

This heavy day begins on the BBC just after 9 a.m., denying us a full day in the park. We want to show respect, though, and to get through all the waiting, we drink a lot of tea. By lunchtime, the boys convert to lager. Meanwhile, Jenny has invented tea-coffee (pronounced 'ti-coffy') by accident, which becomes a running gag alongside many other in-jokes. There's the Tina Turner song pronounced in a Yorkshire accent ('What's love got to do wi yit?') that we've been giggling at for weeks, and there's our obsession with combining odd food items: the utopia of a Cadbury's chocolate finger eaten atop a salt-and-vinegar twirl. A large bag of Doritos is opened with reverence as the funeral gets under way and we gaze in sync at aerial pictures of Diana's hearse speeding along a motorway. We fall into a shared daze that lasts many minutes, unsure whether it's ok to speak. Jenny cracks out a tub of Ben & Jerry's, Phish Food flavour, and the room re-animates to my relief.

Diana's cortège passes under grey bridges packed with crowds and we see onlookers compete to throw their flowers into the vehicle's path, a vein of sorrow flowing across farmland, through woods and snaking around out-of-town shopping centres that look strangely military from above. In our Center Parcs living room, I try not to breathe too loudly. Breathing feels disrespectful. The sound of plastic-wrapped lilies landing in the car's path is the only thing audible above the hum of distant crowds and, in this weird sea of disbelief, I find the lobbing of these bouquets a strangely violent act: Interflora bundles arrowing their way onto a shiny black roof. Slap. A clutch of white carnations wrongly timed and too late. Crash. Snapped stems, torn petals and ribbony detritus along the hard shoulder. Sigh.

In between, we see hushed London streets, the deafening silence only interrupted by the rustle of cellophane. As this strange spectacle unfolds, our eyes rarely meet, for fear of unexpected tears. In solemn rotation, a single white loo roll passes between us, gently unravelling. It is death, the movie, and my friends can't take their eyes off it. Julie's mum, the only adult on the trip, has promised that we will go ten-pin bowling once it is all over. But by mid-afternoon, I am feeling claustrophobic and so I grab my Walkman, untangle my headphones and head out for a ritual of my own.

*

Morrissey is telling me to hold onto my friends. But they are still inside on the L-shaped sofa, still covertly crying, while I crunch across the forest floor, glumly observing a miniature world of remote sorrow on tiny blue screens through chalet windows. A cassette is saving me from all this. I have left the group to their television tears. Morrissey – who wants me to think he too is a fallen saint – supplies my inadvertent Diana soundtrack. He is also my escape tunnel and nature corridor. I am away now, feeling the dew on my ankles and happy to be scraped across the nose by twigs. Morrissey is somewhere out there, probably sneering at all this, but I know he would also love to be deluged by flowers and handwritten notes from strangers. His hairsprayed quiff reminds me, in a strange way, of Diana. For now, it's just me and him, this odd pact, and this tape that is taking me to another place. On one side, the Smiths' *Hatful of Hollow*, on the other the singer's 1994 solo album *Vauxhall and I*, with its collage of mumbling cockneys, dirty streets and boxing gyms. I have no idea where Vauxhall is and can only think of cars. Years later, I will understand that its dark pissy arches are the ventricles through which the blood of gay London flows.

I am fascinated as I go deeper into the woods, afraid of getting lost while absolutely wanting to get lost. I urge the brambles to surround me, I want to stumble into a mossy hole and sleep there. I am falling, with no one to catch me, as Morrissey keeps saying. And as I wander into an area of low shrubby trees, I am pulled towards a different kind of royalty. The voices sampled on *Vauxhall and I* ('They catch 'em, and they say he's mental . . .') paint a picture of an English criminal underworld of hierarchy and respect, but also a world where the Kray Twins demand a Digestive biscuit with their tea. What difference to the aristocracy with their territories and old ceremonies? Westminster Abbey is a boxing club and the state carriage a Vauxhall Cavalier with a roll of fifty-pound notes in the glovebox. As I listen, I want to go to Morrissey's London, one brooding with menace and shadows. I see a damp towel over a tattooed arm, a bruised rib cage through a gap in a door. This is an elite world with a gold tooth, a forbidden audience with some other sort of monarchy. It seems far away from the queues to buy five copies of Elton John's 'Candle in the Wind'.

'You only call me when you're feeling depressed,' sings Morrissey on 'Hold Onto Your Friends', and I shake myself as I realise that the song is describing me, and possibly the contents of my pager with its forlorn communications. In the pre-text message world of 1997, I have developed a habit for paging my contacts (three friends) with not-so-cryptic song lyrics. This hobby brings with it the awkwardness of saying the message out loud to an operator in a call centre. It is excruciating, but I do it often anyway.

The track begins almost too sweetly with chiming, iridescent guitars, a music box opening delicately along its hinges, revealing a warning about loyalty – 'Why waste good time fighting the people you like?' I wonder again about my friends, bonded together and breathing in the bleachy tang of Andrex. Do they eyeroll when I take myself off? Do they wonder where I go? Have they even noticed I am gone? 'Don't be so ashamed to have friends,' says Morrissey. It's me. I am the maudlin one out in the twilight, trying to summon a feeling that I think is more genuine than the sorrow inside. It's me walking the other way down the street, letting my shoulders deliberately collide with my friends. I want them to know that I am bored and slightly lost. I tell myself I am thinking more deeply than them. But eventually I feel a bit cold and find myself craving a Dorito.

20

Make me look like them

I am going for a haircut, and it is the first haircut of the rest of my life. Mum knows of my plan and she is not keen because my long hair, which I wear tied back in a ponytail, is about to become very short hair, which she is still concerned about giving the 'wrong impression'. I think I know what she means. But I put it to the back of my mind, on the shelf with Bernard. The same week, I buy a black leather jacket from a charity shop that must be hung on the washing line in the garden for several days before being allowed to enter the house. It is only a partially successful fumigation; the ingrained whiff of someone else's fags persists to Mum's annoyance. I invent a life for my coat, imagining that this sweet, sickly stench has clung to the silky, now ripped, black lining for at least two decades. It has seen gigs and known other times. A Silk Cut at the Fall. A roll-up at Wire. A pint sloshed onto its cuff at the Slits that left a strange shiny mark. I reach into the pockets expecting to find an old cigarette lighter, but all I can feel is a scrap of paper that turns out to be a faded shop receipt, too washed-out to read the date or to know what was purchased. This jacket is a time machine, I tell myself. In reality, my new-old coat has probably been to a school dance or two and maybe a wedding in a scout club.

I head out nervously to my appointment on the high street, hoping that I will return from the land of magazines and hairspray feeling like the person I hope soon to be. I want to tell the world that I am poetic yet tough, sensitive but able to kick a ball back when it rolls my way in the park. I dream of being Justine Frischmann, Elastica's frontwoman, but with a fragile rage like Richey Manic, the missing guitarist from the Manic Street Preachers. Mostly, I just want to tell the world that my music taste is better than theirs. In reality, I am just a kid with a ponytail and a smelly coat. Inside the chemical world of the hairdressers, I take out the inlay from Elastica's debut album, point at a picture of Justine and Donna, and politely ask Carol, with her blonde highlights and Debenhams top, to 'make me look like them'.

*

'Connection' is a song that enters the universe like an exploding comet, spiralling through the clouds and crashing with bright-red cartoon confidence into a previously grey world. The track is just more than two minutes long and its brevity seems to be sticking two fingers up at the all-male rock bands who expect us to get our lighters out during the encore. I sense that Elastica would prefer us to set fire to the stage and, in falling in love with them, I get a small sense of how it might have felt to be a part of the late-'70s punk scene. The song steals its key riff from Wire's 'Three Girl Rhumba' and I read in the *NME* that Elastica might even be sued for rifling through Wire's post-punk sound effects cupboard without permission. It is such a blatant shoplift it seems hilarious to me, and I think to myself that these blokes from the '70s should count themselves grateful to be dragged into my earshot. When the 'ooohs' kick in a few bars later (soon I will sing them as 'boom!' on indie dancefloors across Leeds), I declare that 'Connection' has the perfect – and sexiest – opening to any pop song that I have ever heard before. The 'ooohs' hang heavy with tobacco stains and lead me towards the car-bonnet sex of the album's next track, 'Car Song'. These tunes do not wait to be liked. They come and grab you by the hand and drag you into a sweaty, surging crowd with good hair. Justine Frischmann doesn't seem to care too much about borrowing from the past to build this future – 'Forget it, forget it, forget it,' she sings with a dismissive tone that I try to copy. She doesn't know why a heart is a spade, but somehow the vital connection is made. Whatever that means, she has me.

I am jealous as hell when Claire gets to see Elastica perform at indie venue Fibbers in York, during the year she converts herself from an All About Eve fan, with a silk scarf in her hair, to a pencil-skirted Pulpette clutching a rum and coke. She tells me about the sweat running down the walls as Justine, Donna, Justin and Annie agitate the tiny triangular stage in a room bobbing with art students. She describes the feeling of being in a crowd that takes you with it, like a tide, and where the floor seems to lift you forwards and upwards, like you are climbing inside the band and them inside you. I think of this and I can feel the bassline thrumming through my ribcage. I am close enough to touch the cables taped to the front of the stage and I want to run my hand along the cool black plastic. I want to be a part of this. This is where I want to be.

The angular mood of Elastica's songs seems to physically fit my skinny body. My arms narrow at the top, where muscles should be, but I know my stringy frame has a place in this scene. I feel connected to people and places I have yet to discover; the song makes me stand a bit taller. When I dance to 'Connection', I keep my elbows close to my hips, which stay taut as I move with a self-aware downward momentum. It is not often that I get the chance to hear *my songs* out loud in a town that is drenched with Kadoc's 'The Nighttrain', so I hijack the CD player at my friends' houses instead. As I move to Elastica (and Suede, and Blur, and Pulp), I want to project a musical intensity, a total immersion in the song. I learn the moves from *Top of the Pops* and I am Jarvis with a pointy finger, Justine staring at her shoes, Brett touching his fringe and Damon lashing the stage with his microphone lead. I am all of them, in a jacket that smells of someone else.

'Connection' cushions my unpopular physique (boys at school call me an 'ironing board' due to my small breasts) against the crushing tide of fleshy, strappy-topped expectation. It helps me survive the handbag house that floods my local pubs, and it bolsters me against the ironic sideways shimmy that I see on Fridays through a cloud of ultra-sweet perfume in the cider swirl of Shite Out. Music is serious and none of us should be laughing, I think to myself, pushing a single, slightly bent fag behind my ear.

*

I am not sure that the hairdresser completely gets the brief. As more of my auburn curls hit the floor, she keeps fluffing up the hair that is left behind, saying something about volume. I am too shy to intervene, but I am gravely concerned by the direction of travel. I want my new cut to look short, but also lanky and effortless, like I've just pushed it back after playing a gig in the back of a pub. My hair does not want to play this game, though, and it keeps kinking upwards. Carol keeps cutting away, with a slightly rogue look in her eye, and even I think it is now getting too short. It is inevitable that Mum will be horrified when I stroll back through the back door, pausing to stroke my cat Alice in my latest attempt at being normal.

The hairspray comes out again and Carol shields my eyes from its toxic tang with the back of her hand. I cough my disapproval (and fear an imminent bouffant) as I stare into the mirror, disliking my own face. I try instead to daydream about the love triangle that jinks around Elastica, Suede and Blur. Wannabe Britpop villain Brett Anderson paints a dark picture of London, the city I imagine myself towards, but I like him anyway. More than anything, I want to hang out by the pool table with Justine and her new boyfriend Damon Albarn. I want to order a pint in the Good Mixer, knowing I am being watched. An hour later and my childhood is in brown loops on the floor. Soon it is swept away, as I stride into a new and airy world, the wind circling my freshly exposed neck. My new cut is elf-like and far from the perfect Britpop fringe that I had wanted, but it is new and exhilarating, nevertheless. I am both worried and excited, but it is too late to turn back. Elastica have given me an escape route from a world where everybody wants to look like Rachel from *Friends*. I cross the road to buy hair products from Superdrug for the first time; gels and waxes in preparation for the long hours ahead, tinkering with my fringe in the bathroom, and pulling my face around, hoping my new look will not only make me look cooler, but older too.

*

On the Bayeux Tapestry of Britpop, right at the start, there is a scene picturing Brett Anderson and then bandmate Justine Frischmann standing together in an underpass at Marble Arch, west London. The future Elastica lead singer is pointing at graffiti on a wall. It reads 'Modern Life is Rubbish'. Further along the frieze, Blur singer Damon Albarn is in his plum Doc Martens on the edge of the Westway, his hand clasping the leash of a bulldog. The dog snarls at the Suede singer. Anderson kicks a can and walks away. There's litter on the breeze. One of these men will make the phrase his own.

In the spring of 1993, just before mine and Claire's pop epiphany in Asda, Anderson had appeared on the cover of *Select* dressed in black leather, his stomach revealed teasingly as his left arm wrapped around the back of his head. Behind him was the Union Jack. He didn't like it but, as we looked at the front cover on the middle shelf in Spar supermarket, we certainly did. 'Yanks go home,' it read, and we felt a ripple of guilty excitement for something we didn't yet understand. Other bands to look out for: Saint Etienne, Pulp, Denim and the Auteurs.

MAKE ME LOOK LIKE THEM

I am fascinated and scared by him as he reaches out for me from between the car magazines. He looks like a girl, but I know he is a boy. I suspect that his nails might be dirty, but his chest is so strangely smooth and clean I am confused. He doesn't exist anywhere in my world: here is an alien being from *the south*; from a basement somewhere with needles on the floor; from a tower block framed by a luminous sky. Brett's body is naked beneath black leather and his hand rests just above his belt. A glimpse of hair leads my eyes to his tummy button, but then I look away with a small intake of breath. His lips are pink against sallow cheeks, his eyes look darkened by wrongdoing. He finds my gaze in the same era as East 17 and Take That, boys that I might conceivably see hanging around by the bus station ('the bussy') drinking lager. Brett is not this: his faintly eyeshadowed eyes take me to doorways through which I will sniff illegal substances on air that also smells of petrol. 'The battle for Britain,' *Select* declared that week in 1993. And in its way, his alien vision led me to the moment I decided to get my hair chopped off.

'Trash' is the launch single from *Coming Up*, the third Suede album but the first that I manage to buy on the day of release, in September 1996. I get the cassette for £7.99 from Woolworths and take it home to play over and over, three years after that first vision of slick, slightly terrifying Brett in Spar. This time I am drawn not to his shiny torso, but to the gloss of the sleeve artwork. I want to join the unreal trio of beautiful people on the levitating mattress; I want to step into the scene – is it a phantom threesome? – and dwell for a time in its impossible neon glow. The song itself immortalises the feeling of being a nobody drifting through a city, skint but dressed to be seen in charity shop clothes and a well-chosen vintage pin badge. You feel lucky as you stare at the map, knowing that being from the provinces is finally a badge of honour. These are the stadium days of Britpop (Brett says *Coming Up* is an album of only top ten singles) and, despite the acrid whiff of burnout, in my nowhere town I am strangely satisfied to be witnessing this glittery hugeness from afar. I want my *Top of the Pops* awash with guitars and I feel proud when I see the *Sun* and the *Mirror* full of drunk indie bands – *my* drunk pop stars – doing unwise things in Adidas zip-up tops. Graham Coxon asleep in his anorak on a traffic island makes my heart swell. For a short while, perhaps just a few days into the summer of 1996, it feels like a takeover. 'Trash' is the anthem of this micro-era: the kids from the art room have carried out the coup and, for now, the popular people in their Fruit of the Loom sweatshirts lie scattered around me in defeat, Mark Morrison's 'Return of the Mack' playing forlornly on a distant radio.

*

Back in 1997, I look for my leather jacket, but it is nowhere to be seen. I ask Mum and she says she put it back on the washing line for further fumigation. But it's not there. All I see is a row of my dad's Y-fronts and some towels with frayed edges, as Alice runs towards me, miaowing eagerly, hoping to be fed. I ask Mum again and she shifts about, saying again that it needed to be aired and that it was making the hall smell of cigarettes smoked ten years ago. She doesn't know that it is me who has been smoking in this coat, freshly imbuing it with the smell of pubs. Mum changes the subject to rage at Tony Blair and what she calls his betrayal over student fees. I am suddenly under pressure because the new Labour government might not give me a grant if I defer my first year in Leeds. Mum is worrying about money and says the new prime minister is letting us down. I am grumpy about this because I have plans for the year ahead. I want to draw things in charcoal, and I want to go to gigs and festivals; this is the curriculum that I have in mind. I never find my coat and remain suspicious that Mum has spirited it away. 'Stolen from the line,' she claims, without meeting my eye. I keep trying to style my hair like Justine and I think often of Brett's leather pose, his angular jaw and ear-ringed ear. It is a jaw I would like to find and kiss.

Secret track 3

The perfect mixtape

In the late '90s, there is no higher art than the creation of the perfect mixtape, which might really be a MiniDisc. Friendships, adventures in kissing and deep lifetime connections will begin this way – in the covert handing over of a plastic box, lovingly labelled, its innards spooled with hidden feelings. Thankfully, and helpfully, the point of these songs is to nearly give yourself away, but not quite. The titles tell a cryptic story: it is you, but the tale will be narrated, sung, played and punctuated by someone else who is really daring to lay themselves bare. When questions are asked – Is she in love me? – your top-left strike might be glad of the deflection.

Through your choices you are saying: look at me, I am thoughtful and smart and a little bit mysterious. On any mixtape, there must be enough weirdness to impress, but familiarity too to ensure your listener makes it to side B. Weird means old, obscure or unexpected; something forgotten, a remix only you know, a tune that might be uncool until your benevolent curation gives it new context. In 1998, my sister Claire makes me a tape that becomes a blueprint for all this, and she calls it Disco Down. *The tracks are listed by hand in black ink, the spine is decorated in blue tissue paper and Letraset text. She creates the cover with a piece of art from a magazine that consists of colourful dots, half-referencing Damien Hirst but more joyful and without the cynicism.*

Claire's mix is art school on a tape: Side A – Roxy Music, 'Out of the Blue' (old, moody, epic) into Arab Strap, 'Here We Go' (unexpected, slow,

introspective), and then Add N to (X), 'The Black Regent' (obscure, definitely weird, bleepiness and hints of creepiness) to the unexpected relief of Pulp's 'Party Hard' (familiar but maintains an important mood of darkness). Later, she throws me Kraftwerk's 'Europe Endless' (forgotten, truly epic, I want to fly along the wires of a motorway), but not before 'French Kiss' by Lil Louis, with its explicit ending, which I have never heard before. On first listen, I blush and reach to fast-forward, but then more Roxy Music, the Divine Comedy and Babybird help me understand that its porno cheesiness is the point and I follow its bassline into a throbbing late-'80s club, aware that things are happening behind dark curtains but unafraid.

A few weeks into my first year at Leeds University, I make a tape for Rose, my new friend, who has a perfect pile of seven-inch indie records in a box by her door. I call it 'The Lupton Concerto in G#', a comedy reference to our scuzzy halls with their locked windows and questionable rodent defences. Rose is in block G, and I visit her often from the drug-dealer wing where I live in block E. The tape is my main project for a whole day, and I push away a media ethics essay about free speech to make way for its production. Using Claire's template, I travel from 'Mario's Café' by Saint Etienne (familiar, uplifting) to the Electric Sound of Joy's 'Total Turn' (obscure: look how cool I am), and sprinkle my selection with fresh but unknown blossom — Sing-Sing's 'Feels Like Summer' — before grabbing Rose by the hand with a soaring known quantity, Pulp's 'O.U.' from Intro: The Gift Recordings, *which we agree is secretly their best album. As I record the track across from my silver CD deck, the 'gone gone gones' bring a tear to my eye and I find that I am nostalgic for a friendship that has only just begun.*

21

Is it asking too much?

The places we go are empty because I have gone to the future. The streets with the pubs are quiet and there is no need for my pound coin on the edge of the pool table. I walk up the high street, the same route as ever, but this time it is to go to work. My job is at Threshers off-licence in an old Georgian building next to Berry's Passage, where Lisa and I used to play the purse game. The old wooden door with its oval windows and optimistic bell will click open, but there's no reason now for me to look up in search of a familiar face. It's not Lisa coming in for a packet of Skips before her shift. It's not Jenny or Julie covertly buying white wine for the party. It will be Mrs Collins coming in with her sloe gin order, and I will have to get on the phone to Schweppes to check on the progress of her soda fountain refills.

I keep my headphones on until the very last minute – this week I'm bouncing between Portishead and Dubstar – and I find that the music creates a tunnel of safe passage from my bedroom into the shop's staff room with its chute down to the cobwebbed cellar. It is my first job to check which shelves are low on stock, especially so on

Monday mornings after the ravages of the weekend. I don't mind this task because it means I get to use the conveyor belt to shunt crates of beer and wine up from the basement, ready to be wheeled around the narrow counter onto the shop floor. I can smell the little rubber fronds on the belt's rotating surface and when Gwen, the branch manager, is not looking, I pick at them around the edges, out of fascination and boredom, leaving a little trail of grey plastic dust, which only I see. I find this secret habit strangely addictive and must ration myself for fear of creating a bald patch. I've chosen this interlude over art college, bored after a fortnight of life drawing in which I've looked at the same model – Rosie, a smiley woman in her early sixties – every day. The teacher told me that the way I use charcoal makes Rosie's skin look metallic. I didn't disagree really, but still decided to quit in favour of earning money to fund my music habit.

When Gwen is not using the landline to call Roger, her husband, she likes to send me down on extra missions into the darkness. She says I'm the best at climbing around the boxes because I'm skinny and always in trainers. I edge my way around solid towers of beer and shimmy across L-shaped blocks of wine in my own dusty game of Tetris, always ignoring the nagging thought that the cellar might be haunted. The stone walls are very old and sometimes feel damp. It is always cold down there. A good thing, I tell myself, for the beer. There is also a constant feeling that a spider might swing across my face, but apart from these terrors, I enjoy being on a *Crystal Maze*-style quest.

When I've successfully located all the items on Gwen's list, I shout up through the hatch. The boxes seem to be holding my weight and Gwen says it is better for me to keep going until all the shelves are refilled. I squeeze through a gap to get to the last bottle of an unusual gin. Then I load up the bottom end of the belt as Gwen edges our cargo upstairs, pressing a big green button for 'go' and the yellow one to pause. There is a red button for emergencies, but so far we've only had to use it once to rescue the straps of Gwen's handbag, which she sometimes leaves on a nearby stool. Today, my list says eight cases of Carling, Stella Artois and Guinness, four cases of Jacob's Creek Chardonnay, four cases of the new Rioja that Gwen says is delicious, twelve bottles of Bell's whisky, six bottles of tawny port and a twenty-four-pack of Mackeson stout for the old lady who always comes in at 9 a.m. on Thursdays. I pride myself on retrieving everything quickly, occasionally shouting up through the hole for better direction if a particular wine is hard to find. Gwen has memorised the layout and guides me remotely into gloomy corners. Sometimes I find a long-forgotten case of wine, to much delight.

When we young ones – me, Lisa or Lindsay – are left alone in the shop, and always in pairs, we like to climb onto the conveyor belt behind the last consignment and ride back through the hatch. This is strictly banned because it puts too much strain on the rollers, but we do it anyway, giggling. I sit with my knees together, looking proudly at my yellow and green Brazil edition Nike Cortez trainers, tucked in to avoid any need for the red button. I hop off once I'm at floor level and grin to Lindsay, who is eating a packet of honey-roasted nuts, at my safe disembarkment. Sometimes a bottle of wine must be written off if it gets jammed and the label gets ripped. We log it in a large book that lives on the desk where we do the cashing up. Once it's been recorded, we are free to 'try it' in the name of research. Sweets and crisps are mostly stored upstairs, and we find a way of helpfully sampling these snacks too; always on behalf of our customers, especially bags of dry-roasted peanuts, which require lots of research, and little green bags of pistachio nuts. Lisa is obsessed with those small Turkish Delights in shiny purple squares, and so their wrappers often get damaged.

*

My Portishead tape sits in the shoebox, calling me back to emotions that I've put on hold while everyone else is experiencing their first term at university. Letters arrive on the doormat – Hélène describes the new friends she is meeting and the dodgy dealings in the flat opposite hers in Preston, Julie's already planning day trips with the people on her course – but I have chosen to live in this strange hometown limbo, for another year at least. I have the 'Sour Times' cassette single but not the album *Dummy* (I choose instead to spend my money on the Charlatans' *Tellin Stories*, and *Expecting to Fly* by the Bluetones), so I am making do with another library bootleg with photocopied artwork; I decide that the spooky front cover works well in the black-and-white murk of a folded piece of A4 paper. 'Sour Times' returns to my ears with a new way of haunting me each time, its trilling dark greys always successful in pulling me under. I know there's a chance of discovering a glittering seabed if I can go deeper. The song has a twist of John Barry, an Italian Riviera mood, so while I turn to it in times of bedroom window sadness ('Nobody loves me / It's true'), it also brings with it a minor-key glamour, of sepia drives along a coastal road under avenues of trees, its descending notes offering teasing glimpses of a twinkling sea.

IS IT ASKING TOO MUCH?

Beth Gibbons' mournful vocal seems distant and undemanding; as she whispers her truth, I find myself leaning closer to my cassette deck to hear her words. All she has left are the memories of yesterday, she sings, as I think of school friendships now pulled like taught threads across the country. Sometimes I play 'Sour Times' at least eight times in a row, returning to rewind the tape, wondering if I have a strange kind of addiction to the track and its depressive mood. It seems to fill me up and to take me in its other-worldly arms, its dark notes both lonely and comforting. Gibbons sings about 'scattered seeds' and 'buried lives', and I think about the meaning of the song and how it connects me to the feeling that I need to go to new places in my head and on the map.

*

On the days when I am doing the late shift, which starts at 2 p.m., I lie in my bed staring at the gig tickets that I've pinned to the slanting loft ceiling – Blur in Sheffield (twice), V96, V97, the Lo-Fidelity Allstars, Manic Street Preachers, Gay Dad and Kenickie – only flipping my feet onto the carpet in time to put on Mel and Sue's *Light Lunch*,[i] which is my new obsession. The old TV set, with its fake-wooden sides and oblong buttons, is now a fixture up in the loft, which makes me feel grown-up. I imagine I'm in

---

[i] When *Light Lunch* becomes *Late Lunch*, Yorkie, Jenny and I get tickets to be in the audience. We meet both Mel and Sue and enjoy chatting to the clipboard boy whose job it is to make us feel jolly in the queue outside the studio. 'Ooh, you've come all the way from Yorkshire,' he says, while asking for our names and finding out what kind of silly artefact we've brought with us. I have drawn Mel and Sue's faces on a large pair of frilly knickers, each of them with their own buttock. The queue boy laughs. I realise later he is Dermot O'Leary.

a studio flat in Camden as I swing myself into position for the hour-long show, which is about food, but really it's about being silly and sarcastic – attributes I think I can match, especially in conversations with Yorkie, who is such a huge fan of the show that she contacts them and offers to create Mel and Sue's website. I'm not really sure what computer code is, but I suspect Yorkie knows about the future. She is the first one of us to get a pager. Robin, the boy who I met at Lo-Fi Allstars during 'Disco Machine Gun', has sent me a message about maybe meeting up in Leeds. I'm not sure how to reply, but it reminds me to play the song on my CD player. I like it because it is slightly unhinged, a messy strobe-lit cider song. I can see again in my head the view of our feet dancing in the gloom of the Cockpit in Leeds; once-shiny trainers worn and battered by gigs, the no-longer-white soles sticking me to a sticky floor with each move. I like Robin because he is the first person I have met who has heard of all the bands I know about, and many more. He seems to have the best record collection on Earth and will later write me postcards, with tiny little words on them, from Paris.

Mum is at work and Dad is always in the kitchen, so I wait until I hear him leaving by the back door to run down for a cup of tea, embarrassed to still be in nightwear. While I'm there, I shovel down a bowl of Shreddies while standing at the fridge, and say hello to Alice, who is miaowing for more food. There's a card on the table for me and I know straight away who it's from by the picture alone: Morrissey in a cuddly jumper lying in a sea of Oscar Wilde books. It's Hélène, of course, sending me one-liners from Preston. She asks: am I as miserable as this man? I go back upstairs and pin the image to the wardrobe by my bed, where Liverpool FC and then

IS IT ASKING TOO MUCH?

a sticker of Take That used to be. Damon Albarn, Graham Coxon and now Morrissey replace John Barnes and Mark Owen. I look at the clock – the clock that has shown me I am late for school so many times – but I don't see the point in getting dressed until my Threshers shift is half an hour away, so I sit in my pyjama bottoms, a trainee student, get back to *Light Lunch*, and chuckle at Mel Giedroyc being mildly sexual about a cheese sauce.

*

I am swimming across a disco floor as coloured squares beneath my feet merge and converge, forever forming new shapes. There's a layer of lemon sherbet across the turntable and every other surface – strange, sugary crystals that I can only feel and taste when I hit play. Seconds later, I'm in a tower block with long views over a silver city. But I'm busy doing housework, hoovering glitter from carpeted corners lit by the drifting blobs of an orange lava lamp. Occasionally there's a sensation of flying through clouds, of swooping over familiar places with strong, confident wings. I am gulping through the air, looking down at traffic islands like the angels in *Wings of Desire*, mine and Claire's current favourite film. I decide to fly down Knaresborough high street and, from up in the thermals, I can see the shop with its familiar door, the woman who always buys Player's Navy Cut cigarettes is just exiting and I almost shout hello as she pulls her tartan trolley over the raised threshold with a bump.

Tears form in my eyes while all this is going on, and I feel a rush of defensiveness towards the woman in Dubstar's 'Just a Girl She Said', who is being plied with drink by a man who does not love her. 'Talk to me, talk to me, talk to me,' she whispers, and it sounds like a plea. 'You can't buy me and take me to bed,' she sings over chords that sound grand like a church organ, but angry and mournful too. 'Pretend you're with someone else tonight,' she tells him, and I want to go to her and throw my arms around her and rush her into the elevator and away, away.

I'm listening *Disgraceful*, the pink album with the vagina pencil case on the cover. It is my go-to soundtrack for train journeys and 'Stars' is the song that seems to work best in motion. Pylons swoosh by, intermittently matching the beat. As they go in and out of sync, I listen intently to the lyrics. *Is it asking too much of my favourite friends to take these songs for real?* I laugh to myself at what Hélène would think of my self-made drama. I have swapped my teenage life for this: staring from windows, from trains and from the skylight, which has always been the place for this sort of mood. 'Sour Times' shimmers with bleakness. 'Stars' is the Hoover bag filled with glitter. The Candy Flip sky I stared at when I was eleven has gone dark.

22

Things worth fighting for

It is a bitter morning when I pull up the blind. The first thing I see is a frozen layer of crystals in a smudge of half-snow across the glass. My childhood self is delighted at the arrival of proper winter, but I am older now and instead I let out a sigh. 'I'm still going,' I say to myself, stubbornly, wiping tiny droplets of icy water from the edges of the window. I have one thing on my mind and that is catching the train to York to find a record shop that will sell me Air's new album *Moon Safari*, which is descending today, 16 January 1998, from a Parisian nebula beyond the horizon. Travelling to another town[i] in search of music is a ritual of 20th-century pop fandom and the geographic chase from small town to city makes the eventual prize all the more satisfying. The quest is spliced with fear of failure (what if other out-of-towners get there first? A *Moon Safari* saloon fight), but it is all worth it when I am feeling the crisp corners of a newly-hunted CD wrapped inside a paper or see-through bag, imprinted with the shop's logo. Jumbo. Rhino. Polar Bear. The train fare is a risk worth taking because I have low-to-zero expectations of my hometown shops ever delivering. Even stadium-slaying guitar bands are not a release-day certainty among the cobbles and Bakewell tart-lined streets of Knaresborough. *OK Computer* by Radiohead and Blur's eponymous album must both be located a bus or train ride away in Harrogate, Leeds or York. I always hold out hope, but feel an expectant kind of dread when I am scanning the new-in racks at Woolworths on the high street, my eyes racing with mounting concern beyond the stacks of Daniel O'Donnell. Occasional bounty comes my way (Radiohead's

---

[i] By autumn, the chance comes to see if Air are real when they announce a UK tour including a night at The Ritz in Manchester. On a Tuesday in November, my sister and I cross the Pennines by train and make time for a visit to Affleck's Palace, the rambling vintage clothes emporium that itself feels like stepping into a dream. Claire buys a '70s shirt with round collars. I look out for Frenchmen in white space suits. The gig delivers: an intergalactic voyage on Whitworth Street West. And there they are, two shadowy figures behind their keyboards as 'Kelly Watch the Stars' sweeps across the audience, six songs in. The album sounds massive and as I blink at the stage, the lights saturated in dry ice, I concede that Air are no longer mine.

'Just' appeared to me like treasure), but more often I find myself standing deflated next to a Celine Dion cardboard cut-out, or stranded to the left of a Boyzone CD tower.

Air have been sending me cryptic messages since Christmas. It begins with a cartoon monkey who loves the moon. She appears without explanation in music magazines in a small white t-shirt and I wonder what she is trying to communicate. There is rumour of a duo from Versailles who are coming soon to change electronic music forever. I can hear the distant hum of vintage synthesisers, like a power station at night, emitting pulses into snowy darkness. The doughnut rings that rotate around distant planets seem to know that they are on their way. A perfectly poured coffee awaits in a side street named after a French queen and soon it will be me watching little swirls of sugar melt into the froth; my brain, my ears, my imagination transported with the same feeling of awe as the boy in *The Snowman* flying over the sea. I'm spellbound by Air's Nicolas Godin and Jean-Benoit Dunckel in their all-white boiler suits, cosmic operatives from another dimension disguised as two mysterious Frenchmen. And still I have not yet heard a note. My pre-emptive excitement has been fuelled by the *NME* and *Melody Maker* who compare Air to John Barry and Kraftwerk, describing an incoming wind of epic strings, techno beats and mournful space piano. I test my trainers, this time my green suede Pumas, in a thick layer of crunchy frost and step into the translucent January morning. I'm on my way.

*

In a nearby universe, I don't know who I am fighting for, but I know there are still *things* worth fighting for because of a song on my sister's new mixtape. We travel dressed in brown nylon with freshly glittered brows and we arrive together at Stereolab's secret mega-hit 'French Disko', which is number one for eleven weeks in a hidden universe between Air's Paris suburb and a newly established encampment on Neptune where everyone must wear a striped top and thick-rimmed glasses. The world is 'essentially an absurd place to be living in,' says singer Lætitia Sadier with a wink. There is an insurgent optimism to her plea and I want to follow her instructions at the earliest opportunity.

Claire loves to craft a mixtape and occasionally she makes a one-off production just for me. Her latest homemade cover is a collage of tissue paper layered over magazine snippets, which she finishes off with black Letraset text. It is Claire's holy communion, this tape, and she has invited me for a taste of the fortified wine. 'French Disko' bounces off our walls and fires me into a mood that is halfway between romance and revolution. I want to march for *something* (*'La Resistance!'*), but I also want to ride away in the back of a vintage Citroën to a cool party where the DJ is called Antoine and everyone is drinking Pernod.

In 1993, Stereolab tuck away their most-loved song on a B-side, calling it 'French Disco'. The song re-appears a year later with a K and now here it is soundtracking my gap year, punctuating my walks up and down the high street with a driving sense of urgency. Like Air, I am in love with the dreamy and hypnotic state they put me in, but energised and ready to fight too. Claire's tape makes formal our shared love of music, which is formed around scrapbook ideas of utopia, cooling towers at dusk and glimpses of Derek Jarman's garden in books (Dungeness seems like a place you might find Stereolab hanging about: thrumming Moogs in the turbine room, a percussive interlude involving shells). Patrick Keiller's mesmerising 1994 film, *London*, narrated by the elusive character of 'Robinson', hooks us further into an imagined world of underpasses, canal towpaths and industrial hinterlands. I imagine Stereolab in these locations, playing a secret gig.[ii]

*

Back in Threshers, I'm working as many shifts as I can to save up money that I will spend on CDs, clothes, magazines and music festivals, to fill up my last summer before university. These things are my main outgoings, along with halves of cider and the occasional bag of chips with curry sauce from the chippy next to the Little Elephant (known as the Little E: yes, this is the '90s). I am finally free of essays and the oppressive cycle of school terms, and find myself gazing serenely across a wondrously blank exam-free landscape. I dream about my history A-level at least once a week, the last vestige of all that stuff. In the dream, I am forever being made to retake the exam, but I never have time to revise.

Kerstin is only fourteen and meant to be studying for her Sats, but instead we spend winter evenings together in the loft watching the old TV with the sound turned down and *Moon Safari* turned up. Each of us clutches a mug of hot chocolate made from a Cadbury's sachet

---

[ii] A few years later, I interview Stereolab for *Leeds Student* before they play the Cockpit in the autumn of 1999. Lætitia Sadier and Tim Gane have a toddler and they tell me, a bemused nineteen-year-old, about what it is like to go on tour with a young child. Later, in November 2011, I find myself watching Lætitia playing a solo set at a fundraiser for at my daughter's nursery. It is a complete surprise. Then I see her son, the 'baby', and he is sixteen.

bought in Spar supermarket on my way home from work. Sometimes we add in little floating islands of pink and white marshmallows, and, very occasionally, a burst of synthetic snow from a can of squirty cream. It has become a ritual and Kerstin sometimes puts in a chocolate bar or sweets order ahead of my return. Peak luxury is a packet of Munchies, which we savour in their little squares, one by one, as we sit back on the uncomfortable sofa with its itchy brown cushions. Our current obsession is watching the Winter Olympics live from Japan. The time difference means we get to watch the action into the night, and we find ourselves mesmerised in darkness as 'La Femme D'Argent' or 'Talisman' appear to sync perfectly with the downward swoop of a slalom skier or the triple Salchow of a short man in tights from Canada. Mum calls up the stairs to say we should be getting to bed soon. I mumble 'Yes, in a minute,' as I reach for my hot drink, which is now the perfect temperature, with its gentle spiral of sweet foam. Kerstin and I look at each other, dunk half a Twirl, and settle down for the curling, which is finally made exciting by our French electro soundtrack.

'Sexy Boy' is the single that announces Air to the universe a month into my love affair with *Moon Safari*. The lead track seems to describe our two new heroes – 'unshaven but well dressed' (*Où sont tes idoles / Mal rasés, bien habillés?*) – but it's not clear if the lyrics are really about them. The song is everywhere and the whispered words 'sexy boy' make Air an overnight British sensation on *Top of the Pops* and breakfast TV. Dad says he is reminded of the faux outrage that met Serge Gainsbourg's 1960s song about sex, 'Je t'aime moi non plus', and I nod my agreement. I'm worried, though, that Air are perceived as a novelty act and not the new frontier of dance music that I know them to be.

In my sky-gazing room, I am genuinely glad when the hype around 'Sexy Boy' dies down and I get Air back to myself. I am looking beyond the chimney stack at the stars above our house on a cold, clear night and connecting them in a giant game of dot-to-dot. Clouds shift in milky-blue bands, obscuring the brightest pin pricks of light for several minutes at a time. I sit in the darkness waiting for the stars to reveal themselves again and during this waiting phase, I look down at the houses along the skyline, all of them with the lights on, television ghosts on rhomboid ceilings. I can just make out the roof of Lisa's beyond the green lamppost that we used to climb up to get across the cattle market. Nobody is looking out or looking up. It's just me here with the rustle of nesting birds, and the music.

'Kelly Watch the Stars' takes me on new expeditions with each listen. I am Kelly and Kelly is me. The stars watch me as I watch them. Huge intense eyes beam down from the single's cover, and I am thrilled when I manage to get hold of a promotional poster (another town and country mission) for my bedroom wall. Like Daft Punk in their mysterious masks, there's a sense that Air might not really exist. A French hoax. A band from *Button Moon*. The big eyes twinkle on a dark-pink background and the middle eight takes me to the milky way.

Despite their cryptic beginnings, it is Air that will soundtrack the end of the '90s, not Oasis or Robson & Jerome. By the close of the decade, *Moon Safari*'s atmospheric fingerprints are everywhere: in the wing mirrors of new cars, on the radio in Spar as I buy Kerstin another Twirl, and whisked into the sauce of every TV food show that tries to evoke luxury and adventure. Nigella Lawson is in her kitchen observing the progress of a crème caramel to the sound of 'You Make it Easy'. Jamie Oliver slices an onion to 'Sexy Boy'. The album still travels everywhere with me in my headphones, and will soothe me into my own new worlds. By the summer of 1999, there are finally copies of *Moon Safari* in Woolworths.

23

Rave marmalade

With Claire at Pulp in Finsbury Park, a month after Glastonbury and finally mud free. (Photo: Alison Denholm)

Every time I jump, I feel a slosh of fresh mud go over the tops of my wellies. There is very little defence: my doubled-up socks are long abandoned to the inevitability of the situation. Any part of me that is somehow not damp is coated in a crisp shell of recently dried dirt, sometimes in spatters, at other times a smooth and consistent dusting, as if I am a finely crafted chocolate, only one with an unfortunate and acrid agricultural scent. The rain is in my eyes and in my mouth as I squint towards a twinkling stage. Claire and I have been planning these days for weeks and now we find ourselves on the inside of the anticipated moment. Yellow lights bubble up from the horizon into a dark-blue sky. A pyramid glimmers. Around me, the surge of 100,000 bodies, and ones just like mine in soggy clothes, stumbling with unstoppable but slow momentum through a stinking swamp. This mud is no ordinary mud, it is Glastonbury mud and it smells medieval. I don't know it yet, but its unique stench will stay on my clothes and in my nose for many weeks to come. Perhaps it will stay forever.

*

We arrive at the outer hedges of the festival during a break in the rain on Thursday afternoon, the pale sun offering hope as we wind our way by foot from the shuttle bus that picked us up from a station that sounds like a place in a fairytale: Castle Cary. We are walking optimistically with carefully packed rucksacks on our backs: in mine a sleeping bag, four t-shirts, a pair of jeans, over-trousers, plastic bags, bin bags, Primula Cheese sandwiches in foil, Mini Cheddars, a can opener and things to wrap other things in when everything inevitably gets damp. The forecast has been worrying us for days and so we have also brought special tent pegs that promise to keep us upright whatever the slimy state of the earth. The tent itself is shared between us, a handle each, as we descend a farm track that is already concerningly squelchy. We're on the lookout for signs of the most famous musical gathering on the planet – a billowing flag, an inflatable marijuana leaf, the thud of a distant bass. In the end, the first sign of Glastonbury is a farm boy riding bareback on a white horse. He leans down and asks if we would like our bags to be taken inside for us, promising to drop them off near the Green Fields for the cost of two pounds. Claire and I look at each other, shrug our agreement quickly, and then watch our backpacks sail off into the distance, our shoulders gifted twenty minutes of freedom.

We've had our tickets for weeks. I have been checking on the whereabouts of mine intermittently for a while, even though it has never moved from its spot pinned next to my ticket stub for Blur at Sheffield Arena and Oasis at Knebworth. Now, finally, we are presenting them to a smiling woman in a yellow tabard at one of seemingly hundreds of gates with big black numbers above them. This is it: we are entering Glastonbury, our feet at last on sacred, sloppy earth. We drift into the site, wide-eyed, and happily find our bags tottering on top of a huge pile of luggage brought in by the horse boy. We strap ourselves back in and, seeing for ourselves the extent of the famous Pilton mud, decide that we must hike to higher ground. The only problem is that 95,000 other campers have had the same idea.

We begin searching for anything resembling green grass in order to pitch our tent, but the main camping areas are already brown and boggy. We keep going, soaking in the circus mood of the Green Fields, and the general defiance against the rain. We find ourselves considering a wooded area, but it is too good to be true; we realise it is already being used as a makeshift toilet zone for people who fear the portaloos. We press on, eventually finding an area with just enough dry-ish ground to begin unpacking our things. The compromise we are forced to make is pitching our temporary home very close to a performance tent, and partially across a pathway. In desperation, and as the rain starts to fall again, we begin pulling out the super pegs that will keep us alive for the next four days. As Claire is busy pushing them in with her foot, it's my job to begin curving the main poles into position without twanging them into my sister's eye.

During this slightly tense process, we are interrupted by a man with a white bucket who appears next to our tent with a manic sort of grin. 'You girls want some acid marmalade?' he asks. Claire looks at me and I look at her, smirking and unsure. We stand up and peer into his gungey orange gloop that is smeared with finger marks. 'Err, maybe later,' mumbles Claire and we smile to each other at her half consideration. 'There will be no later!' he replies with an impish flourish and carries along the path looking for other customers. When the tent is up, we climb inside and giggle at the horse boy and the rave marmalade, already aware that we are now living somewhere between the A37 and an imaginary world.

When we emerge, we look again at the big top that is just a few metres away. We have a map of the site, already crumpled, and we are both peering at it to try to work out where we are when I turn the map around again and, squinting at its eastern side, realise that we have camped in the Field of Avalon. There is a blackboard at the door of the big top with tonight's performances chalked up next to little drawings of daisies. My eyes seek out the headliner: Ozric Tentacles, 10.45 p.m. I have never heard of them, but Claire says they are a hippie band and mumbles again about acid marmalade. I don't know whether she means everybody will be on it, or that we will need it. I look down at myself in royal-blue Adidas tracksuit bottoms and green wellies. On top, I'm wearing my Menswear t-shirt and a navy-blue cagoule. I realise that I am not dressed for the hippie quarter. The Green Fields are still relatively green as we walk through on our way to explore the paths to the main stage and dance arena. Very tanned boys with golden dreadlocks sit on hay bales with mud splashed up the lower half. One of them throws a lighter into the air and it seems to somersault slowly before landing gently in his friend's cupped hands. The boy doing the catching is in trousers so large that the hems are already completely destroyed in ragged muddy loops that trail to the ground onto brown, formerly white Vans. His feet must be soaking wet, I think to myself. We carry on and consult the Glastonbury programme that was handed to us at the gate. It comes with a lanyard with all the stage times on it, and so we hurriedly stuff the A4 booklet back into Claire's bag to keep it dry. We scour the itinerary, already with must-sees in mind (Blur, Pulp, Underworld, Saint Etienne) and make plans to be at the main stage in time for My Life Story who will begin the festival at 11 a.m. on Friday.

*

I'm walking through rooms in a house that I do not recognise, but the spaces in between keep turning into the set of *Supermarket Sweep*. There is a turnstile on the Victorian door and the kitchen has been converted into a bar selling rows of Red Stripe cans, with a shelf above full up with cocktails, all of them fizzing with red or yellow liquid. The whistle at the start of the tune calls both to my guts and to my legs. It is as if Bez himself is ushering me into a secret party, except this isn't even his band. The walls undulate between shopping aisles, boxes of fish fingers, stacks of canned soup and a wallpapered hall with an umbrella stand. I reach for a row of ketchup bottles, which, as my hand makes contact, becomes a wooden banister. Primal Scream's 'Don't Fight It, Feel It' booms between rooms, its soulful undergroove reaching around the walls, making me mischievous.

With its cartoon splodges and laughing voices, the song gives me the feeling of travelling through an adventure inside the pages of a graphic novel. I am jumping between colourful squares looking for the doorway to the next part of the story. There's a Scooby Doo stupidity, a frantic party energy, but then the track melts into an urgency that demands more seriousness. *I'm gonna leave the life I live. I'm gonna love the life I live.* I'm space hopping back to the Green Fields, clutching onto a bloated orange creature with a grinning black face, but I am also gliding towards a place where I begin to hear the whispered call of someone who wants to kiss me.

The piano break at three-and-a-half minutes has me dancing on a podium with my long-sleeved t-shirt tied around my waist, my bouncing feet squeaking into pools of gleaming sweat. There is no podium, however, it's the arm of a sofa. It feels good up here, I feel strangely secure, and the people sitting cross-legged on the rug beneath don't seem to mind. Nick looks up and smiles his approval before returning to a production line of near-constant Rizla preparation. I jump down with an attempted theatrical twist and tell Nick how I watched Primal Scream at Glastonbury from the top of the hill, with a view of the whole site, and how I can still smell the mud. 'Smoke this,' he says. 'It will eradicate the mud ghosts in your nose.' 'Thank you,' I smile back, before basking in the playfully percussive piano groove that swells like a sunflower growing in fast forward, turning its face towards the light.

*

RAVE MARMALADE

Waking to first light on Friday, I unzip our flimsy fabric door and blink in disbelief to see that every other tent in the Avalon field is under water. By some impossible stroke of either geography or mystical ley lines, we are the only campers not submerged. A member of staff in yellow is using a megaphone to direct flood victims to the welfare tent where sleep-deprived festivalgoers can go to sleep in rows as temporary refugees. We know we are the lucky ones. Glastonbury 1998 feels like our Woodstock, and despite the mud soup, which means we cannot sit down for four days, we find ourselves on a near-mythical musical journey, fitting in as many of our favourite bands as we can; a kind of frenzied dancing spree taking place in the survival zone of a disaster movie.

We plan our afternoons and evenings meticulously, agreeing our strategy in advance and being strict on any cider-fuelled hints of deviation. If we leave Tori Amos after half an hour, we can catch the end of Marion. After Blur, let's run to the Other Stage for Underworld, but for this we must sacrifice Cornershop. These borderline military operations involve many miles of careful trudging, sometimes along pathways so deluged by gloop that the signposts and markers at the edge of the track are entirely submerged. But we know the route now and we spur each other onwards with the promise of a good view of Kenickie. Our biggest concern is the fear of leaving something we need at the tent; there is simply no room in our schedule for retreat. Claire's Jordan's cereal bars meet this fate and are later found floating in puddle.

During more rain, we find a tent showing the England World Cup match against Colombia. Claire goes off to buy two beers while I find myself staring in wonder not at the players – Paul Scholes nearly scores inside the first two minutes – but at the dazzling greenness of the mud-free French pitch.

In between our sorties to the four main stages, we buy punnets of noodles for three pounds. These are served in a generic brown sauce with an occasional slice of carrot. Chips are two pounds. Our eating pinnacle is a hash brown on Sunday morning and, to celebrate this culinary high, Claire orders two cups of tea, which come in polystyrene cups dusted along the edges with powdered mud. We gulp it down anyway, glad to have a small plinth to lean against along a wooden shack that looks so wet that it may already be rotting. A pint of lager is £2.50, which means both food and drink can be procured for around a fiver. We ration our drinks to minimise the need for a portaloo once we are in position at one of the stages. A no-man's land of rogue pissing has evolved between the Green Fields and one of the central paths to the Pyramid Stage, which we cave into using ourselves, despite saying it was disgusting on day one. All the dandelions smell of wee. It is a bad idea to let any bit of clothing touch the ground.

We are on our feet, permanently. A log upturned near the swamp outside the main dance tent brings occasional sanctuary. From this spot, which is very rarely free, an unkind spectator sport has evolved that involves watching unsuspecting ravers plunge into a hidden sink hole which lies, concealed, to the left of the tent's main entrance. Those that succumb find themselves in mud up to their thighs. We see a girl try to style it out by pretending to swim and we say a small prayer for her underwear.

The days are gruelling as we wait for the cool twinkle of night. We roam around looking for adventure among dotted encampments of firelit raving. After Blur and Underworld on Saturday night,

Claire turns to me, grins, and says we are floating on vast biblical lands of mud. This is a one-off experience and one that we must never forget. I meet up with Robin, my nearly-boyfriend, by mistake, in the middle of nowhere. He has just been pick-pocketed and Claire tries to save him from being shoved around by men pretending to be marshals. It is not the marmalade scene anymore, but soon enough we are back safely in a bog, watching Blur. Damon dedicates 'End of a Century' to Judy from Richard and Judy. 'I was watching on Monday and she kept running off set and being sick or something . . . This song is about that sort of thing, and I was worried about her . . .'

The only time we are not standing up is when we have crawled into our tent following complex manoeuvres to stop our feet from entering the hallowed, mud-free inner sanctum. But it is around this point each night that Ozric Tentacles kick of their show, which features the bassiest bass I have ever heard. As I try to doze, Claire stays on guard to physically catch the bodies of stumbling revellers as they inevitably trip and come careering towards our tent. We switch over our sentinel duty as often as we can, which means we are shattered as we listen to more heavy rain and even heavier basslines from the Tentacles.

*

Jarvis Cocker is dressed in a TV detective's coat that is reminding me of Columbo's beige mac in the American crime drama. It is not the '70s nylon shirt with the pointy collars that we have come to expect: this is a different version of our Pulp frontman. He taps his microphone and exhales wearily, and I sense that there is a mental weight pressing down on him, a feeling of burden upon the shoulders of his creased coat. Orange triangles of light shift around the stage as drummer Nick Banks beats a steady and familiar rhythm. Jarvis seems momentarily forlorn as he gets ready to embark, again, on one of the biggest moments of his performing life: singing the song that will define his career to 100,000 faces in a field, and one of them mine.

At thirty-four, he is already the elder statesman of indie; no longer the clean-cut debutant of 1995, back when Claire first implored me to come downstairs to watch him sing this song to the Glastonbury masses. Three years ago, there was a leaping joy in Jarvis's stack-heeled step as Pulp performed their surprise headline set instead of the Stone Roses, who had pulled out a few hours earlier. This time, Jarvis's hair hangs in a sweaty basin cut as he stands, gasping, breathless in the knowledge that now is the time, once more: he must do it all again for us. I look at Claire and Claire looks back. This is what we came for. Around us, everyone seems to feel the same. The last of our lagers and ciders are swigged and we are all ready to travel with Jarvis like we used to. If only he would take us by the hand and run with us through the long grasses at dusk, the city twinkling behind him, to go on a bus ride just for the fun of it – from Intake to Broomhill – and feel the weight of time slowed down to the speed of the dust specks lit up by the last rays of summer sun. But Jarvis's arched eyebrow has given way to a furrow of bewilderment. I get the feeling that the world he once craved – neon lights, wealth, an invite to the Brit Awards – is no longer the one that he wants. This Jarvis is no longer telling us jokes about listening to Scott Walker in a fish market, and he's not making us laugh with stories of the dusty horse and dray on his mother's mantelpiece.

Claire and I have picked a route to the first six rows, our feet a sodden mess again, but our faces angled upwards hopefully into the night. Finally, there is no rain. We are close enough to the front to bathe in the pink glow of the stage when we hear the pulse of the song that we all know is coming. Like Christmas Day, I half push it away, wanting it so much but fearing its arrival will mean it is all over too soon. 'There is one thing I haven't said yet,' says Pulp's frontman, standing with his back to us, his right arm extended and his hand making a fist. He is summoning the pointy, sweaty, flailing-limbed Jarvis that we all demand. The volume leaps when guitarist Mark Webber plays the most anticipated notes of the weekend: the opening bars of 'Common People'. And then Jarvis Cocker punches the night sideways.

It is the song about the posh girl at art school with the lyrics about screwing and pool: it's the class war song that makes us dance and grin and want a rum and coke. 'I want to sleep with common people like you,' she says, and we don't know whose side to take. Jarvis is back with us, his foot on the amp one minute, skittering across the stage in his all-beige outfit the next, jabbing his finger passionately towards the crowd, perhaps aiming it at us, who think it's all such a laugh. This is not a celebration of the ignorance of the Greek girl; in its way, it is an accusation that we don't get it either. *You'll never fail like common people.* We slide away into a flailing sea of muddy hands and legs. Still we'll never get it right, even if the chip stains and grease come out in the bath. The idea of a bath seems like a distant dream as we walk back up the hill to the sound of the chorus being sung again by little clusters of invisible campers.

'Common People' is the soundtrack of sixth form and one of the only tracks that we don't argue over in the common room. It is playing when I make an escape from the sweaty darkness of Sly's nightclub in Ripon after half kissing the boy with blond curtains again. It is the song that takes me through fast getaways from teen dramas in Hélène's red Citroën. We laugh at the state of other people's love triangles – we call some of them 'love rhomboids' – because we have pick 'n' mix strawberry laces in the glovebox and we have Jarvis.

Hélène writes poems about our art teacher looking like Bryan Ferry and listens to John Peel, but because she is more sophisticated, she does so on Radio 4, not Radio 1. Hélène seems to be half grown up, certainly compared to the rest of us, but always manages to make me giggle just when it's a bad idea – often as we are walking into assembly or during a very quiet still-life drawing exercise (it seems often that we must draw a ram's skull in charcoal) with our other teacher Mrs Noakes who we call Biddy. Her real name is Bridget and there's a rumour that she is secretly a dame. Our secret is that she is probably our all-time favourite teacher, but because she is too cool to care about that sort of thing, we never tell her. Biddy wears her hair with a punkish grey fringe and her only footwear seems to be black pumps, the type we used to wear for PE in junior school. We note her bias towards us girls, especially during coach trips when we get handed barley sugar sweets first (the boys must wait) because 'our blood sugar levels are more prone to dipping'. We have no idea if her science is correct, but we take the benefits gladly.

It is Hélène who I wander around town with when we are old enough to be let out of school at lunchtime. We lose ourselves to a terminal laughing fit when Hélène buys a giant chocolate chip cookie that contains a long brown hair. This grim finding –

the 'hair cookie' – becomes a part of our sixth-form folklore and because we find it so hilarious, we never even go back to complain. We don't want a refund; we just want to cackle until we are gasping for air and pleading for the other one to stop being so funny. Most of Hélène's handwritten letters to me – some of them left in my locker, some of them actually sent via the Royal Mail – begin with the words 'oh lord' and frequently contain the phrase 'any road'. Hélène sends me Pulp lyrics – and I think she loves Jarvis nearly as much as my sister.

*

When it's all over, we take a little green bus back into the world we know: teashops, supermarket car parks and the squeak of a shopping trolley across cobbles. Our exit from the festival site – by foot, through muddy lanes, for miles – has nearly broken us and I am doubled over in pain, my stomach muscles no longer able to hold me up. It falls again to Claire to take the strain with the tent; we come close to leaving it in a hedge. But we keep smiling to each other at the things we have seen. A rainbow over the stage for Saint Etienne. Our faces warmed in the golden sun of Robbie Williams at dusk as we belted out every word of 'Angels'. Nick Cave wooing us under a glowering sky with his backdrop of gothic blood-red trees. Claire is exhausted from her overnight heroics preventing another drunk person from crashing into our tent. Now that we are riding through normal streets, with pavements and places to pause, we can't quite believe our eyes. We spy park benches with a covert thrill, turning to each other to say 'ooh, that's a nice dry one', before remembering that the real world is full of dry seating.

CONNECTION IS A SONG

Our old teacher Mr Robinson has offered us a place to stay and recover, and so we catch a connecting bus from Wells to Cheddar and enter a quiet, clean world of pleasant streets with things we need on them: laundrettes and shops with no queues. Fizz gets us fish and chips and mushy peas, which we eat in his clean, spacious home with proper knives and forks. Neither of us is balancing on a half-muddy tree stump eating brown noodles.

24

Happiness is dancing

With Steve in Rose's room before a night out. Note the poster for Pulp's *His 'n' Hers* behind us on the wall. (Photo: Rose Jenner)

I have escaped in the nick of time from a sea of Topshop dresses and disposable tuxedoes. Summer is over. My job selling booze to old ladies is done. I am with my oldest newest friend Steve, who I have known for all of my first week at Leeds. Our conspiratorial approach to university life is evolving fast and in our days together we have already decided we will take over the music pages of *Leeds Student* newspaper and ensure ourselves a steady flow of free CDs, entry to gigs and the inevitable glory that will come with writing beautiful prose about our favourite musicians. In our first grand gesture, known only to ourselves and our new flatmates, we agree to shun what we believe to be the mainstream horror of the Freshers' Ball with its threat of blue alcopops and ironic dancing to B*witched. We are certain that we want nothing to do with it and so we find instead a breakbeat night at The Faversham, which we've been told is where the cool people in big trousers congregate.

I first spy Steve stretching out on the lawns beyond my window in our halls of residence at Lupton Flats in Headingley, which is wondrously just a bus ride away from the various Leeds concert venues I've been willing myself towards for the past few years. No longer do I need to worry about missing the last train home, no more must I push my way out of the crowd during the encore to get to the cloakroom and the doors. Our flats are three-storey 1970s blocks with plain windows that initially make me think of prison, but I send the thought to the back of my mind as I see my new neighbours pin up tie-dye throws across their doorways. In our rooms, which are around two metres wide, brown hessian curtains hang limply, scratchy to touch. I assume Steve is a second year because he exudes such an easy confidence and seems to be settled already as the rest of us shunt boxes of possessions up the dirty white stairs that smell of weed. Mum helps me bring things in and never notices the pungent aroma. Instead, she fixes me nicer curtains (green, William Morris) and goes around the corner to Wilko to buy me a washing-up brush and a dish rack.

HAPPINESS IS DANCING

I spend my first, shy, afternoons tinkering with postcards, pinning my allegiances to the wall in a strange mash-up of '60s design, Blur and Saint Etienne posters, and a picture of Richey Manic showing the camera his infamous '4 Real' arm wound. I've brought some of my favourite ticket stubs to put up in the hope that they will impress my new peers – Blur, the Manics, Kenickie – alongside an image of my favourite pop icon Dusty Springfield, my ironic inflatable rabbit, which I got from a stall on the pier in Scarborough, and a carefully curated selection of Northern Soul flyers. On my bookshelf there is a row of Ian McEwans and a well-thumbed copy of Douglas Coupland's *Generation X* turned frontways to make me look post-modern and smart. Later, Steve will lend me *Microserfs*, which I add to my literary display. Around about this time, Mum finishes fixing up my curtains and stops worrying briefly. She joins the gentle exodus of parents who press payphone cards into our hands as they depart, looking back at us like freshly hatched chicks. We wave and promise to call often, although it is clear already that the queue for the phone box is to become a feat of endurance.

Finally, we gather in the kitchen to make one of two things: noodles or pasta, on a small Belling hob. I am trying to look casual as I pretend that I cook for myself all the time. When we visit Steve downstairs, he is tasting a tomato sauce in the sophisticated manner of a top chef, gently adding more spices before re-assessing his culinary creation. I have so far managed to stir a packet of instant pasta shells. Our flat on the second floor – my room is E222 – is not yet fully occupied, so it is just me and two Amys to begin with, one from Bath and one from Nottingham. They will become Amy North and Amy South, although I immediately question the northerly status of Nottingham and both Amys laugh. They have been here a day already and inform me that the shared bathroom might be haunted and that there is both a carbon monoxide scare and a rumoured squirrel infestation. We don't know which is the reason for us not being allowed to fully open the kitchen windows, but our shared sense of injustice gives us something to talk about. This chat continues as we edge around each other and then sit down at the white, rectangular laminate table. Amy South brings a CD player into the kitchen and puts on Massive Attack. The boys venture upstairs and we make them cups of tea before learning that our bit of Lupton Flats is already becoming well known due to the smell of weed that begins to rise up the stairwell each day from around 11am. One of the boys at the source of this scent, Rupert, is apparently available to 'sort you out' whenever needed with whatever you need. We snigger at being in block E.

Steve has been allocated the room directly below mine, which means I can shout down to him when both our windows are open. Later in the autumn term, our vertical closeness proves unfortunate for him when, after a night watching Abba impersonators Björn Again at the Town and Country Club (a dangerous lurch to the mainstream), I get so drunk that I come home alone early in order to deal with the hellish sickness by myself. I lie on my bed, willing the spinning ceiling to leave me alone, turning away in revulsion from the blow-up pink rabbit. When a new wave of nausea sweeps through, I find I don't have the time to make it to the poltergeist loo, so in a state of panicked emergency, I decide instead to lean from the window and send an arc of cidery puke through the night air and onto the grass outside Steve's room. He is in, listening to a Faze Action album, and reports a waterfall of vomit passing by and a vision of me in bright-green pointy collars. I am still in my pretend disco outfit when this indignity strikes. I apologise the next day and swear to never go near cider, or the 1970s, again.

We know that our halls are the cruddy ones for state-school kids (nearby accommodation with gardens and Tudor beams seem to be exclusively occupied by privately educated rugby fans and people who play the cello), but our flats are centred around dance music. We drift from room to room, the boys on the ground floor, the girls on levels two and three, and hear Rae & Christian blend into Red Snapper, Grooverider overlapping with Fatboy Slim. Drum 'n' bass paints our walls, with a fug of smoke between. My room remains the guitar indie enclave, at least at first, before I take up being a raver after Christmas. We live next to a group of nursing students who seem to do the most drugs. When I'm in their kitchen, I spy their 'shag chart' next to the fridge: a point for a snog, two points for sex and three for staying the night. We snigger but do so slightly in terror. When I go back, I notice their tally has increased.

One day, the boys in Steve's flat play a prank on one of their flatmates, Nick, by putting all his furniture outside, reconstructing the layout – including his desk and computer – perfectly, but on the lawn through the window. When he doesn't come home in time and it starts to rain, the joke starts to become a worry and so we hurriedly bring all his stuff back inside, this manoeuvre led largely by the girls. When Nick gets back, he is none the wiser to his belongings having been a brief studenty art installation. The prank that actually sticks is the day we watch the boys wrap absolutely everything in their kitchen in tin foil. They've bought nearly every roll in Wilko in their mission to turn their living quarters into a strangely alien environment. The toaster, the kettle, every pan and wooden spoon turns silver. Even the table and boiler are eventually transformed. It makes visiting their quarters an experience akin to the Roswell incident. Steve's other flatmate Rob has a tattoo that starts off as a slim black band around his wrist. A few weeks into the autumn term, it has become a solid black sleeve that runs all the way to his elbow.

Steve wears baggy Evisu trousers and Nike trainers with fat tongues. In his flimsy student wardrobe, I glimpse twenty pairs of trainers lined up in neat rows and decide that this is what I want to do too. I elect to save up and become a better trainer connoisseur. The first university-era pair I acquire are bright red Adidas SL72 re-issues from the Schuh sale – and I am in love. My hair is styled with V05 gel that goes annoyingly crispy, but it is the only way my hair seems to stay in the sub-Britpop shape that I have cultivated for a year and must now maintain. Instead of the ball, Steve and I settle into our breakaway night at The Faversham, a student stronghold with a mood of fag-ash dusted beanbags and low-slung jeans. With every minute, our anti-mainstream choice feels more right because we're not queuing up for Bacardi Breezers or dancing feebly to music that we hate.

*

I am dancing to a band known as BRA and it feels as if the dance-floor is made of pillows. 'Bentley's Gonna Sort You Out!' is rippling across the room like a ruffled duvet, its whistling tumble-weeds giving way to soft, bleepy hills that draw me from this lazy, sleepy world along hot tarmac to new places, perhaps a rodeo with a cactus in the foreground, but perhaps also a helter-skelter that takes its passengers to a giant ball pool on the outskirts of Birmingham. Either way, this is where I want to go because I know that happiness is dancing. I feel far from the tacky carpets of Jimmy's in Harrogate and the leatherette booths of Shite Out in Knaresborough. These places are only seventeen miles away, but now that I am here, they could be in another solar system. I have already travelled light years.

Bentley Rhythm Ace are DJing at The Fav and playing their own song with its lolloping, groovy beat. I grin at Steve as the tune carries us into the middle of the room, through new shapes of lights that overlap and intersect on the floor like a giant kaleidoscope. We are moving in time together to what we soon describe as drunken toddler big beat. The track interrupts itself with dozy brass, squiggly electronics and a whimsical, cream-cake vocal – 'I looove it'. We draw in the air with imaginary crayons, sketching out an evening of new beginnings, and then we hitch up our big jeans to the sound of a bouncing spring which catches the soles of our trainers with – 'Dong!' – another Beano-ish sample. This wonky, cartoon electronica captures perfectly our current mood. I have run away from my hometown, the ball and my pointy Suede shoes.

I am swimming in clouds. I'm in a desert and I have just spied a cactus. I leave Steve for a few minutes to order myself a half of Coca-Cola, which turns out to be the most sensory Coke of my life. I crunch the ice cubes like a visitor to earth experiencing a cold drink for the first time. I roam, joyous and free, and I keep wanting to stop to chat to strangers. They all seem receptive enough. They laugh when I tell them that I have a strong urge to do a GCSE maths paper, right here, right now.

'Bentley's Gonna Sort You Out' is a Midlander rave anthem that I am only now discovering in Leeds, a cartoon club hit that lives alongside Fatboy Slim's 'Praise You', and is born from a very English, indie pedigree. One of BRA, Richard March, was a former member of late-'80s Stourbridge grunge-pop act Pop Will Eat Itself. His co-conspirators Mike Stokes and James Atkin had also rattled around the *not London* alternative scene, with Atkin a member of early-'90s baggy act, EMF, who hailed from rock 'n' roll paradise Gloucestershire. There's a provincial swagger to the track, and their former bands, which seems to emanate from the same faggy back rooms of pubs as Britpop.

The song is accompanied by a deliciously lo-fi promotional video in which the band play swingball in shiny shirts and then drive around in a Mary Poppins-style vintage car, before making Bentley waffles in some sort of imaginary catering van. Then everything zooms backwards, and the Bentley boys are landing parachutes in Laurel and Hardy reverse. It is deliberately clownish from the Birmingham duo and the kind of video a bunch of students might dream up while doing a bong. Less than a week into university life I have found my new tribe.

*

Boards of Canada are performing their big single 'Roygbiv' on the *Top of the Pops* that exists only in my head. They have stormed the ambient charts and won the battle of downtempo electronica. Now their vintage synthesisers, with their syrup-like digital elixir, drip their bounty all over the imaginary stage, and I am standing in the audience, mesmerised by waves of emotion that *feel* blue and green as they shimmer around me and then find their way right through me. The track is instrumental, except for a child's voice that is both spooky and innocent when it intermittently says 'Lake!'. It is hypnotic and nostalgic, and an addictive substance in my Lupton flats bedroom. I wish to find the lake and dive into its watery willows.

I find the band and the track through the rivers and streams that I travel down with Steve – the quiet-loud electronica that he loves and that seems to offer routes into new parts of the musical cosmos. This understated celestial anthem is one I continue to devour, but hardly ever with company. It is a solo experience and reminds me of my days gazing from the loft window back at home. The group – who are in fact from Scotland – mix vintage synths, odd samples of distantly babbling children and hip-hoppish beats that trip over themselves. It is Four Tet scrabbling around with a drum machine under your school desk with De La Soul.

As 'Roygbiv' casts off again, its darkening keyboards give way to an ice-cream van sweetness that I find myself hooked on. The track is short at just over two minutes and so I loop it repeatedly on my CD player with its special MiniDisc slot. I've recorded myself a late-night electronica mix that I listen to while half-writing essays about media law cases from the 1980s, often, and oddly, involving Julie Burchill. The disc also features Kid Loco, Kreidler and To Rococo Rot, but it's the gently hallucinogenic undercurrents of Boards of Canada that reel me back endlessly. As 'Roygbiv' plays in room E222 for the twenty-fifth time this evening, I join the queue for an ice pop that is made from frozen mountains. 'Roygbiv' is a mnemonic, its letters stand for the colours of the rainbow, and so I taste blocks of vivid colour in between its icy layers. It is an epic soundtrack that brings to mind both ospreys swooping on river prey and an aerial view of a blinking high-rise city. I want to be one of the mysterious people on the cover of the album that it comes from, *Music Has the Right to Children*, in their sun-bleached world that is washed in a green and blue haze, until I notice that these figures have disturbingly blank faces. I decide instead to take a dream-like airship voyage across a green city. When I dare to look down, I see silver streets glinting in the morning sun.

*

In Freshers' Week, I make a beeline for the gigs, but I do so in my Manic Street Preachers t-shirt that reads 'Hell is Other People' on the back in silver letters. I am not sure that this is the best approach to making friends, but it seems to draw a smile from certain types, and especially boys with a hint of eyeliner. Another t-shirt leads me to another new best friend. I am standing at the bar in the back room of Milo's nightclub in Leeds city centre, hoping for a glimpse of tonight's DJs. We have been promised Tim Burgess of the Charlatans and Sarah Cracknell from Saint Etienne, but so far there is no sign of them and it is past 11 p.m. I'm wearing my tight purple t-shirt with big eyes on the front from the cover of Saint Etienne's single, 'Sylvie'. I'm glancing at my watch again when Marion taps me on the shoulder and says 'Hi, I like your t-shirt'. She is the first person that I have ever met, other than my sister Claire, who seems to know everything about the band, and via glamorous means. Marion explains to me that she found Saint Etienne through her Norwegian boyfriend at film school. This seems impossibly cool, but I try to not to look too much in awe. We share our disappointment at Tim and Sarah's no-show (they never do appear), but find that we are still chatting, and dancing, many hours later when the club calls time. We swap our new Leeds University emails in the hope of meeting up, although I am still unsure how to use mine. I buy an '80s t-shirt in a charity shop in Headingley. It's an old ballet top in soft beige and across the front two figures leap for joy. The slogan, in blue, reads 'Happiness is Dancing'. I start to wear it more often than 'Hell is Other People'.

25

Steal your name

With Rose (*left*), Marion and Andreas at a Leeds University Union night. (Photo: Antonia Dietmann)

There's a screech from the tumble dryer end of the laundry room opposite block E in Lupton Flats where huge metallic cylinders rotate our clothes in froth. We sit along wooden-slatted benches waiting for the machines to bleep, but it takes a while, and so it forces us to shake off our shyness and make conversation with people from the other buildings. It is clear that this is the first act of solo clothes washing for many, although – as with the cooking – everyone's trying to feign experience with this sort of thing. Amy South is folding her big combat trousers, the ones that she wears with ragged hems over her Buffalo trainers that add two inches to her height. Amy North has already piled up her pale pink towels with efficiency and is waiting for the rest of us, smiling and twiddling a red-blonde curl with her finger.

The sudden flurry of laughter is because a pair of black lace knickers – so far unclaimed – have come out entirely shrunken: not wrecked or melted, just absolutely tiny. These weird doll's pants have undergone a very strange metamorphosis and probably because they are made of plasticky nylon unable to withstand the industrial heat of the dryers, which seem built for NASA and not for our underwear. This comedy moment is too much to bear and as news of the micro-knickers travels more widely, communal hysterics circulate in increasing waves. This goes on for a while, attracting passers-by who divert their journeys – most of them were on their way to join the pay phone queue but this is potentially more entertaining – to find out what is going on. Even Rupert the downstairs stoner shows an interest, putting his head around the door and smirking before delicately placing a freshly rolled spliff behind his ear and shuffling away in his worn-out checkerboard Vans. Just when we think the microscopic briefs are not that funny anymore, we are gone again, snorting with the hilarity, gazing again at their miniature perfection, tossing them between us for another disbelieving look. Nobody knows whose they are. It is eventually deduced that they belong to a third Amy, from block G, but she is nowhere to be seen and therefore cannot deny or confess the charge. I decide I will make enquiries with my newest new friend, because I know that she lives in the same flat.

She comes from Bedfordshire, she is sarcastic, political and has the promotional poster for Pulp's *His 'n' Hers* on her bedroom wall. In her own way, she *is* a Pulp song, and she certainly is to me. We meet during an indie disco at the union on day three of our new lives in Leeds. She is doing Jarvis pointy fingers on the dancefloor, and so am I, and so we end up pushed closer together by our separate groups and arrive in the middle of everything.

Others are enjoying the scene because we are both in '70s-ish nylon shirts (mine is green, hers is black) and moving our Cocker-ish elbows and wrists to coincide with each other and the first chorus, as if our joint dancefloor invasion were a planned event. My fellow Pulpette laughs as she frames her face with her hands and flutters her eyes upwards, as Jarvis does in the video. In response, I go big with an inverted L-shape – sticking my arm out awkwardly, but very Jarvisly, for a final flourish. We all fall about drunkenly and breathlessly, and I am relieved that the next song – Republica's 'Ready to Go' (the DJ wants his kebab) – is not a must-dance tune. We mumble things about Lupton Flats and squirrels, making a mental note of each other's blocks. We bump into each other again, both of us clutching wobbly pints of lager before last orders. We make a plan for me to pop round to hers the next day or the day after. I tell her I'll come to hers. I'm trying to keep it cool but really I am suppressing my delight at finding a music comrade.

*

I'm edging my way slowly towards block G, which is round the corner from block E, along a diagonal route that splits like a letter Y to link up the furthest flung parts of our halls. As I walk, I look down at the weeds peeping up through the cracks in the ancient, pockmarked concrete and I think about all the other student feet that have walked this way before me, in Doc Martens, in battered black leather Adidas Gazelles, in white slip-ons or maybe in barefeet after a covert scamper to another flat. The mostly neat grass verges, with occasional dandelion clusters, remind me of my grandparents' old house, which is just down the road in Headingley but now stands empty of their things. I think about the dense and strangely mysterious cobwebby bushes at the edges of the garden where, in her 1950s childhood, seven-year-old Mum once searched for a dead starling after hearing my grandparents discussing a radio report confirming the death of Stalin.

I remember the long grass that we cut together after Nanny's death, Mum wiping away tears between new bouts of effort under unexpectedly persistent West Yorkshire sun. We had only one pair of shears and so we took it in turns to use them, with their shiny black handles, before swapping over, the other trying to make headway with kitchen scissors. I recall being proud of myself for helping her, but being surprised to see her upset and choosing not to say anything in the hope that my uncomplaining assistance was support enough. As I stroll down this path, I find myself thinking about all these moments. I'm there again in my grandmother's bedroom where I used to feel mournful at the sound of a distant motorbike. I think of Grandad Bert throwing me a rubber ring, that was really meant for a dog, and I feel again the joy of successfully catching its clammy form in my four-year-old hands.

Here I am, still in Leeds. In fact, I am back in Leeds, where I was born, but now I am in another dimension. I hope that my grandparents can see me walking confidently along these cracked slabs towards times to come. In this same nostalgic moment, I hear my future self telling me to stride with joy towards a friend who I will still know and love in twenty-five years from now. The shared joy of music is the silky golden thread that pulls me into the hall of block G that smells of fags and stale lager. The connection is always a song, I tell myself, with a fleeting feeling that I have worked out how to exist. This one starts with a comedy dance move during 'Common People', and it takes me to My Life Story.

*

A harpsichord trills my ears into a state of expectation: I know that this song comes with batting Venetian fans, glittered eyebrows and beads of sweat that will, with any luck, transform upon my cheeks into fine white pearls. I have the t-shirt already: 'My Life Story' embossed in gold on red, bought at the Cockpit before my regular sprint for the last Knaresborough train, just a few months ago, in my old life. The song starts with an urgent mood of greasepaint and drama before a frantic drum roll ushers in the first verse with its swerving hips and lip service and its motorcycle driving south (a journey I will make, and sooner than I realise). I am staring at the front cover of My Life Story's album, *The Golden Mile*, and as I listen, I am entranced by the image of speeding traffic. Headlights turn into gleaming threads that are pulled along a motorway to a destination that promises cocktails and dangling earrings, suits and shiny boots. It is a place that will not keep still and all of it is trapped inside a small polaroid square.

The song accelerates with spiking violins that push me upwards towards a vaulted ceiling, below which singer Jake Shillingford sits upright on a deliberately ridiculous and ornate throne. It has golden edges, but is painted with cheap nail varnish. Jake perches on a frayed burgundy cushion, his kiss curls look like marzipan, his brow damp with the endless high emotion. It is from this place, in my mind, that he sings this song to me, and it is almost a Christmas carol – '12 Reasons Why I Love Her' – with its list of things that make the boy love the girl. Jake's vowels are both estuary and Drury Lane, he is a lad in a Ben Sherman who is leaning on the fruit machine, chewing gum, but he is also a port-sipping actor in a silk waistcoat, arching an eyebrow at the scruffiness of everything. The track is already an ode to nostalgia, with its park benches etched with the names of teenage loves, but it is funny too and that is the main reason why we keep replaying it, a self-declared shopping list of love, as we sit on the edge of the narrow bed.

We skip the CD back and listen again, this time focusing on the lyric about pies and greens. The girl in the song doesn't eat the pie, only the vegetables, which we decide to mark her down for, while chuckling and lighting up another cigarette. My new friend says she fancies a boy in a band who acts a bit like Jake and says that he is confident enough to wear shiny trousers in tiny rooms in the backs of pubs and that's one reason why she likes him. I suppress the fact that I have never dared fancy anyone in a band who I might conceivably meet.

I first spy '12 Reasons Why I Love Her' among a pile of seven-inch records in a box on the floor where I also glimpse Suede, Gene and Longpigs. I nod approvingly, but secretly my heart does a small somersault. This sort of thing just would not happen back in my hometown, in the land of Jamiroquai and Hooch. We chat more about music, and also about her course, English Literature. Her tutors say students must read a book every week, which sounds like a lot to me, and to which she says, 'will probably put me off reading forever'. My course, I explain, is semi-vocational – Broadcast Journalism – and I say that I know 'vocational' is a dirty word but, trying to match her dry wittedness, I say that I don't care because I'm going to get a job on the radio while everyone else ends up in PR. We move on to more interesting matters, namely our weakness for boys in eyeliner, and we chat about David Devant and his Spirit Wife and their song 'Ginger', which I have on a compilation given to me by my sister and which I promise to share soon on a mixtape. We make plans to see Rialto who are playing the student union on Wednesday, and I tell her I will bring round my CD copy of 'Monday Morning 5:19' beforehand so that she knows at least one of their songs. We also arrange to meet up with my other new friend, Marion who, I explain, has more Saint Etienne CDs even than me, and has the best indie band haircut you've ever seen but without realising. We know we are going to be friends. But there is one big problem. I have forgotten her name.

I have been trying to let my memory do a background search, a bit like Alta Vista, the computer thing we've been learning about in college, but no results have been returned and the situation is getting critical. I am forced instead to hatch a plan that feels low-key criminal but convince myself that this is the kind of thing that happens in songs. I'm going to steal her purse in the hope that something inside will reveal her name. If she catches me, this will be my defence: I was just writing an imaginary Suede B-side.[i] Before activating my desperate operation, I wait, hoping for luck to intervene. I am willing one of her flatmates, such as tiny pants Amy, to walk into the kitchen and simply say her name. This moment, of course, never comes. I am left staring at the dozens of club flyers pinned to the wall, my mind spiralling. I prepare myself to pounce on *anything that might save me from this embarrassing hell.*

My friend makes more tea and while her back is turned, my hands creep across the table towards her purse, but I abort the mission as she swings back to face me. We put on *Neighbours* on the small grey TV at the end of the Formica table and I find myself relaxing again at the sight of Madge arguing with Harold. I am biding my time now until she needs to leave the room. We dunk our custard creams together and chat about upcoming gigs. I tell her about mine and Steve's dream of writing for the student paper. All the while, my eyes keep landing back on her wallet that surely has her student

---

[i] A few years later, a drama involving a purse intervenes again in my friendship with Rose. We are stumbling back to our tent together at The Big Chill festival at Eastnor Castle in Herefordshire. Rose spots something lying in the grass – someone's wallet – on our way to see Mylo. Rose picks it up and, because we're in a hurry, we decide to do something about it later. After dancing to Mylo, we remember the purse and unzip it to see if there's a name. No luck, so we decide to hand it to a steward near to our campsite. But we have a dilemma: inside there is a £20 note and two ecstasy pills. If we hand in the pills, are we getting whoever owns the purse into trouble? We ponder taking them out, but in the end we just hand it all over. The next afternoon, as we are dancing in pale sun to a band called Crazy Penis, the Rave Gods find a way of thanking us. Between songs, frontwoman Danielle Moore stops to chat to the crowd. 'I just want to say thank you,' she says, 'to whoever handed in my purse.' Rose and I glance across to each other, beginning to smile, as Danielle continues. 'You didn't even steal the drugs. Ha ha!'

card inside. We both drink tea by the gallon, which gives me hope that a loo visit will come.

Finally, it happens when the doorbell goes. My hands trembling, my heart racing, I lean across the table and fumble open the clasp on her purse. It feels like it takes forever, my fingers inept, but when I eventually get it open, I immediately see the holy grail: a shiny, laminated card and on it my friend's face, her name printed beneath. Rose – *Rose! Rejoice!* – stares back at me from a Woolworths photo booth and I'm sure I can see her eye-rolling at my ridiculousness. Then Rose walks back into the kitchen and offers me a cigarette. She puts on her Gene album, *Drawn to the Deep End*, and turns up the volume. We listen together in silence for a few minutes, and I know that I am breathing too heavily for someone who has been sitting still.

*

Martin Rossiter's pleading voice, with its very English vowels, seems to cut through like none of the other singers we are gazing at in *Select* magazine. As he delivers his lines, I look up from my mug of tea, placing it carefully next to a tottering pile of paperback books – the top one is *Brave New World* – on the varnished desk that is built into the wall of Rose's room. I feel very aware that I need to concentrate on the Gene singer's earnest message to me, and so dunking my custard cream (Rose and I have quickly established a shared love of cheap biscuits) during the chorus might be a distraction. 'I am still young,' he says, 'my blood flowing like a flood.' 'Fighting Fit' is playing from Rose's CD player as she deposits ash along the window ledge. Despite the enforced locks, she has managed to fling hers wide open. The air outside smells autumnal and for a moment I think of Dad collecting firewood just a mile or so away where we used to live on Woodland Park Road. This is Leeds, the city in which I was born, but it feels like a brand-new place. This is my new world and so I swing my attention back to the record.

Rose's next boyfriend is in a band, and her best friend back home is a musician too. She is telling me about all the gigs she has been to in London – trips to pubs in Camden, the Electric Ballroom, Barfly, the Water Rats, names I have only seen in the *NME* – and it all seem to be perfectly normal to her. She is telling me about the Thameslink and night buses and how the Good Mixer used to be good but that it isn't now. I ask her if she ever saw Blur there, or even Menswear, and she just laughs. 'Nobody's all that bothered by them, Anna,' she says with an almost teacher-like tone (both her parents are teachers, I learn later). We chat about Gene and whether they are too much trying to sound like the Smiths. We agree that Oasis are essentially a Beatles tribute act, we give Blur a reprieve for having 'gone a bit mad in a good way' since they sounded like the Kinks (now they sound like 'moody Americans,' Rose says, I think she means Pavement). Martin Rossiter does look a bit like a young Morrissey, we agree, with his nice hair and intense gaze.

Rose's flat is usually full of ravers, the ones that actually live there and others who seem to drift through on their way to somewhere else. The flats up the road, James Baillie, seem to be our twin halls and, like ours, contain a mix of high-achieving caners who didn't get their first-choice accommodation either but now they feel glad about that too. We crouch around in bedrooms with burn marks on the carpet, listening to Rae & Christian and asking after green skins. But then we mostly seem to get our essays done too. Rose's flatmates are always talking about the previous night's pills: how strong, how mellow, how trippy, how crumbly, how cheap. My flat is an enclave of Bristolian chill-out (Massive Attack, Tricky, Portishead) punctuated by visiting nursing students (all of them always on a bender of some sort) and me blasting out a mix of guitar bands, strange electronica and '60s music down the hall. I go through another Dusty Springfield phase in the spring and, when I learn of her death, I cry all afternoon. Steve pops upstairs to try to console me and mentions a Chemical Brothers gig coming up that we should try to go to for the paper. I mumble my agreement before getting back to Dusty. Her voice seems to go with the droplets of rain streaming down my window.

When I shut my door to try to get an essay done on the Canon StarWriter (which my parents have let me bring to Leeds; it still reminds me of Mr Robinson), Blur's *13* becomes my late-night soundtrack. Rose and I both go out to buy it from HMV on the same afternoon: she gets the regular CD and I buy the white box-set. She's into Graham Coxon and loves his painting on the front cover. Our new friend Marion gets the box version like me; we are suckers for nice packaging. The album is bookended by emotional anthems, opening with 'Tender' and ending with 'No Distance Left to Run', and these songs paint the dirty cream walls with a mournful blue at my end of our flat. I wander out into the darkness to give myself a break from an essay about Rupert Murdoch's influence on general elections. I put my head around the door to the laundry room and see that the tiny pants are still pinned up on the noticeboard.

26

Lords of the trance

Reading *Leeds Student* in bed in my room at Lupton Flats.

Steve has to persuade me to try out for a music-writing job at *Leeds Student* newspaper. Despite my earlier fighting talk, I do not dare audition on my own, but we feel confident together and it turns out to be an important trap door into a secret world of midnight curry orders, phone calls with pop stars and surreal late-night missions to the hangar where the paper is printed, one of us clutching a single terrifyingly corruptible disc containing all of that week's edition.

The music editors – Sonja, Oliver, James and Fiona – make me feel like I am starting a job at *Melody Maker*. They are ever so slightly aloof, and James has intimidatingly cool hair. He wears a vintage flight bag diagonally across his chest and might conceivably be persuaded into eyeliner, while Oliver is tall and blond and dresses all in black. Sonja and Fiona arrive last and are chatting to each other about someone called Dave from Pomona, who has been on the phone again. I learn later that he is something called a music PR and that he sorts out press appearances for bands. *Leeds Student* seems to be top of his list, which works out well for us. By the end of the year, we are all on regular speaking terms with Dave and surrounded by towers of free CDs that he has sent to us in slim white jiffy bags that squish beneath our trainers on the office floor. Sonja is the smiliest of the editors: she nods when I'm speaking and I notice that she really looks into my eyes. I realise too that she sounds exactly like Jo Whiley when she is on the phone trying to secure an interview with the Beta Band. Fiona seems more shy than the other three, or possibly more scathing about our newbie ambitions. As she pulls up her snowboarder-style trousers, she tells us to sit tight and explains that they will be back in a minute to show us how things work.

After a nervously silent wait in the corridor outside the newspaper office, we make small talk about Freshers' Week (we all agree it is very embarrassing to be offered fruit-flavoured condoms as we try to swerve being recruited by the badminton society) as we sit on square upholstered seats pushed against grubby cream walls. I am in my red Adidas zip-top and trying to look like it is feasible that I am in a guitar band. Steve is more relaxed in big beige combatish trousers which bunch up over the fifth pair of trainers I've seen on his feet in as many days (Vans, grey, with chunky white laces). Finally, the foursome re-appear, each of them clutching a chunk of CDs, and we are put at ease with a joke about who will review the Savage Garden album (after a tumbleweed of dread, the answer: no one).

These second and third years exude a self-belief that makes me want to match their seriousness and maybe even win them over with my talent for comparing music to biscuits. We are required to write a test review[i] and I take on this task with a steely determination. Steve ponders the Jon Spencer Blues Explosion CD but eventually goes for Kruder & Dorfmeister. I choose Black Box Recorder and set about describing its songs through the medium of motorway service stations, graveyard flowers and Rich Tea biscuits. A few days later, the most intense of the four editors, Oliver, emails me back to say he enjoyed my writing. I am more delighted than he will ever know. This must be how newly signed bands feel in their red tracksuit tops.

Steve and I both get a gig. We are now staff writers on a newspaper with a circulation of 20,000 copies a week, which is potentially

---

[i] A year later, when Steve and I have ourselves become editors and auditioners, a boy called Tim is trying out for a slot, just as we had done twelve months before. He says very little and I hardly notice him other than to observe his Oasis-style fringe. His test piece turns up a few days later and it is beautiful. He becomes the man who upsets Morrissey on behalf of the *NME* a few years later and then becomes the *Guardian*'s culture editor.

more readers than the population of my entire hometown. I am thrilled and I make it my signature style to use as many unexpected comparisons as I possibly can (cooling towers, the smell of petrol, more biscuits) to describe the songs that I love, while savouring the chance to be incredibly rude about the ones I do not. I compare the Stereophonics' output to a fart with big eyebrows. Oasis are 'simple, simple boys'. When Six By Seven release a track called 'Eat Junk Become Junk', we scrap our regular vox pops with Leeds students and instead ask a packet of crisps, a Mars bar and a can of Coke for their views on guitar indie. The CDs of bands we do not rate are ceremonially flung from the office window without care for innocents who could be hit by the flying debris of a weak third single. Later, we find them on the pavement outside in little crunched-up, silvery shards. Runston Parva, the first incarnation of Leeds' homegrown boys Kaiser Chiefs, suffer this fate and I spot their promo single smashed on a verge as I queue up for chips outside the Met's indie disco, Star, the next Thursday night. I feel a pang of guilt about this when I remember that the drummer, Nick Hodgson, sold me my favourite Adidas zip-top – the navy blue and light blue one with elastic armpits – at the second-hand shop, Blue Rinse, next to the Corn Exchange. He worked there when I was sixteen and was on duty the day I was upset at not getting Blur tickets for the Town and Country Club. He had missed out too and he made me feel better about it.

The *Leeds Student* office looks a lot like the set of *Press Gang*, the early '90s TV show about the fictional youth newspaper, and this pleases me enormously as I step inside on day one as a music writer. Experienced journalists (second years) sprawl across the desks on swivelling threadbare office chairs with the upholstery hanging out in yellowing clumps. Reporters in t-shirts and jeans reach for their notebooks, grabbing a pen from behind an ear, shunting themselves across a coffee-stained carpet on reluctant black plastic wheels and entangling themselves in phone cables, just like newspaper hacks on TV. I hear a boy with a curtain fringe calmly tell whoever is on the other end of the line that 'you have until 5.30 p.m. to submit your right to reply'. I pretend that I am used to witnessing this cool, tough coalface of journalism, but really my pulse is racing.

There are piles of old newspapers everywhere. Some of them higher than the desks and about to initiate an inky landslide. Beneath the tables, which are contoured with clumps of dry chewing gum, lie abandoned pizza boxes, odd shoes (a single Nike Air Max trainer with no laces), tea mugs stained brown, and thick twisty cables bound with black tape that travel between six computer terminals through a subterranean network of dust and unread promotional books. There is a tower of CDs leaning against a wall, each with a folded piece of A4 sticking out – the record label blurb, I learn later – so I quickly work out that this is where the music team gathers. Sonja arrives with her bouncing step, dressed in a black-and-white striped top and holding a vintage-looking satchel. She takes out a bunch of CD singles and pushes aside a takeaway box to make space, while apologising for the mess. Sonja then points me towards a metallic grey filing cabinet with five alphabetised drawers. Inside, she explains, we can find a large selection of press shots of the bands and musicians we might end up interviewing, or slagging off. These are the pictures they want us to use, not the ones we might snap from the front row at the Cockpit or the Duchess. I pull open the second drawer at random and it skitters outwards on rails that make a cringing, scraping noise. We all wince, but the bounty inside is good. The first thing I see poking out in the A–C section is Cerys from Catatonia. Below her I can see Dodgy's logo peeping out – boring! – and a glimpse of the Dandy Warhols, yes please. Soon I will be taught how to scan these shots into the Apple Mac computers with their colourful sides, before importing them – Apple E! – into our pages, which always feels like the most fun part of the process. I am told about the importance of a kern, the little gap between the big letter at the start of a sentence and the rest of the word. Forgetting the kern is a rookie error and makes everything look crammed together. From this day onwards, I will never forget to add my kern and most of the time it is the very first thing that I do.

*

I am standing on the flyover that runs between Leeds University, where I am a student, and the Met, where the newspaper office is located. I walk this way often. It gives me a natural border between my two new worlds and my two new circles of friends: my course mates and my *Leeds Student* colleagues. I feel like I have known the newspaper crew for months. We eat together (free curries), go through 'disc error' crises together as deadlines loom, and – after another computer crash – sometimes even sleep in each other's company on the black, squashy office couch.

On this autumn night, I am looking over the edge of the bridge near the Met and into the rush-hour cars as they nudge their way home. A stream of red lights blurs away into the distance and out towards real Leeds: Chapeltown and Harehills. The sky is pale blue and smudged with a bank of grey at the point where the buildings on the horizon meet the sky. My headphone wire dangles and my MiniDisc player, which I hold with my hand inside a pocket, is warm and buzzing slightly against my palm. In my ears, on repeat, I am playing 'Midnight in a Perfect World' by DJ Shadow. The song trips over itself, its fat trainers moving in slow motion across the curved sweeps of concrete that meet the pavement. A distant female voice soothes my grey edges.

There is a sense of resignation to the track, a shuffling and depressive quality, but despite this there is a snow globe optimism too and it is this whirling hopefulness that makes me stop and look up. A flock of pigeons takes flight across the car park near the hospital where I was born. I imagine Mum there in the freezing cold January of 1979, clutching me and asking the ambulance driver to go more slowly across the ice. I think of my sister Claire, then four, awaiting my arrival at home, sitting patiently on our brown settee. Back here in my new Leeds era, Claire works at CD Warehouse on Merrion Street just five minutes away. I often pop in and sometimes I can hear the shop's sound system as I approach from three doors down: Claire and her future boyfriend Pete playing Abba at top volume, just for the laugh.

This new geography connects me to old geography, the routes I take with these fresh soundtracks connecting me to childhood. Later, I will race my flatmate Adam from our address on the edge of Hyde Park into Leeds city centre, him convinced that going the direct way along the road is quicker, while I argue in favour of a diagonal route through the university campus, as the crow might fly. We both promise not to jog, but to keep a steady and even pace. We converge about fourteen minutes later, at the town hall lions, both slightly breathless. We never do truly agree on who got there first.

Back inside the DJ Shadow song, a pebble-dashed bollard gets in my way as I imagine the track in liquid form, pouring across my new-old city like slow-moving tarmac. A glimmer of evening sun is snuffed out by clouds as the piano refrain loops towards its melancholic conclusion. Its ticking clock and stuttering sample – 'N-n-n-now, n-n-n-n-now approaching midnight!' – create a darkening mood. I stand still, staring at empty windows in office blocks, wondering about the lives of the people inside. I start taking buses around Leeds for no other reason than to help me listen more intently.[ii]

*

Steve and I make it our mission to interview as many bands as we can when they come on tour to Leeds, and especially the ones we know we like. It means I get to ask obscure questions of Stereolab ('Do you take Tommee Tippee cups on the tour bus?'), Alpinestars ('Can you ski?'), Super Furry Animals ('Are your trainers more interesting than your music?'), Saint Etienne ('Who is Maurice?') and Goldfrapp ('Can I have your chips?'). I spend so much

---

[ii] Riding the circular routes that spin around the whole city become a primary way of listening to new songs. The road connects me to the music and the music connects me back to familiar places. I find it is the perfect way to listen to a whole album and I start doing this with new releases before writing my review. I don't have a portable CD player, so it is a labour of love copying albums across to MiniDisc.

time doing things for *Leeds Student* that my course leader, Judith Stamper, pulls me into her office to ask me if I think I should do less journalism in order to concentrate on doing more journalism, but for my degree. I am slightly baffled at the question, but she is a Yorkshire TV legend – and one I grew up with every night when she presented the news on *Look North* – so I don't have it in me to answer with anything other than a meek 'Maybe, perhaps'.

A few months later, I add a show on the student radio station, LSR, to my list of extra-curricular weekly activities thanks to the encouragement of a boy called Rowan who seems already to be an *important person* at the station, and is a contributor to the Manics fanzine, *Repeat*. I am completely starstruck by this fact but manage to keep myself together. When Judith learns about my new radio commitments, she gives me a severe look before turning down the main corridor of the Institute of Communication Studies (ICS) in her squeaky leather trousers with an unspoken disdain. I think I've lost her goodwill, but I shrug my shoulders and set off to meet with Steve because we need to start planning the track list for our upcoming show, which goes out between midnight and 2 a.m. on Wednesdays. This week I intend to play 'French Disko' to start our programme, *Little Big Tunes*, while Steve wants to play 'Sound of da Police' by KRS-One. Our friend Lisa records the show for us and after we come off air, we go round to hers to listen back to the whole thing with cups of tea and cigarettes.

I never miss an essay deadline, so I'm not sure what the problem is with Judith, but it is also true that we develop a fraudulent technique for buying an extra couple of hours' writing time. The hand-in system in the ICS requires us to staple a time-stamped covering note to our work before it is posted through a letterbox into the tutor's in-tray. To avoid losing marks for lateness, we take it in turns to send one of us running from the library to the stamping machine in the nick of time, ten minutes before deadline, before sprinting back to hand out pre-stamped sheets to those also in on the deception. This allows us to breeze by later and drop in our finished essays late but not late. Even more cunning operators stick their hand into the slot to lift up others' work and place the late hand-in beneath those genuinely dropped through on time, so as not to arouse any chronological suspicion.

Back in the newspaper office, I am on the phone again to the record label people who say they can get us access to bands and musicians who are coming to town. Occasionally we are offered phone calls instead of face-to-face chats with the bigger stars who are on tour but who are not yet due in Leeds until after their single or album is released. On a Thursday lunchtime, I find that I have agreed to do this kind of interview with the mystery man behind Ibiza mega-hit '9 P.M. (Till I Come)'. He is called André Tanneberger.

*

Waves of synths float over me like first sunlight falling onto a gently undulating sea. My body feels light and my hair falls across my forehead in such a way that I feel like I am in a pop video. The air tastes salty and the breeze comes in through the half-slid-open window in billowing soft sheets that feel like they are just for me. I stare into the lights on the road ahead, which move around like dancing diamonds in the rain. My short-sightedness (which I am still ignoring) makes the world a kaleidoscope of colours and interchanging shapes; seeing things too clearly spoils the chance of imagination. Blobs of water run down the glass and inside each one I spy a miniature and beautiful world into which I would like to step. I am soaked in Balearic bliss, headphones in, cap pulled down, and all of this on the top deck of the 97 bus on the way to an important phone date.

Soon I am in the *Leeds Student* office, my twelve questions written down on a note pad and waiting to be put through to ATB by his well-spoken manager. Tanneberger is still on tour in Germany, but will be coming to Leeds on a tour of UK student venues in 1999. This suddenly feels more nerve-racking than going backstage before a gig, when the artist is usually distracted by bandmates, tuning an instrument or eating. There is an intimacy to this, and it is making me nervous. I'm not sure I can summon my usual sarcastic style of questioning, and so this proves to be the case. The line clicks and André says, 'Hello Anna', and I say, more formally than I intend, 'Hi, and thank you for taking my call'. My interviewee is extremely courteous and polite, and, as feared, this pleasantness jeopardises my snarky student journalist arsehole persona. I do not have it in me to poke fun at his single hit tune and I wimp out of asking him if his song is essentially about sex. I lose the question about his favourite cocktail and drop my enquiry about whether he would consider entering the Eurovision Song Contest, which seems to be in my head purely because he is German. I have a word with myself. In any case, I absolutely love '9 P.M. (Till I Come)', especially now that Steve has converted me into a full-time raver. If only they would play it at the Mint Club where I now spend Saturday nights with strangers in the chill-out room.

André tells me about his family's move from East Germany into the West before the fall of the Berlin Wall and I am hanging on his every clipped European vowel. 'I'm a lucky man from a brave family,' he says down the line, but oh so clearly, and I definitely do not want to tell him that his song, with all its personal meaning, will only be heard around Leeds by drunk people at the end of the night, or maybe on the radio of a kebab van. 'I feel the music takes me to places inside myself that I could never otherwise go,' Tanneberger explains, earnestly. I scrap all my silly questions and tell him that, as a listener, I feel exactly the same.

When it comes to writing my piece, I convince Naveed, *Leeds Student*'s editor, that it needs to be the full-colour centrespread of *Juice* magazine, the arts and culture part of the paper (and the bit everyone actually keeps, for the TV listings). Naveed agrees immediately and congratulates me on finally writing about music that people actually dance to on Friday and Saturday nights. 'No more of that weird stuff you like, Anna. I'm proud of you!' Together we start brainstorming the headline. Naveed gets there first and, with a broad, mischievous smile, pushes himself away from the desk on his plastic wheels, punches the air and says, slowly: 'Lord.......! Of. The. Trance.'

27

Moby's bus

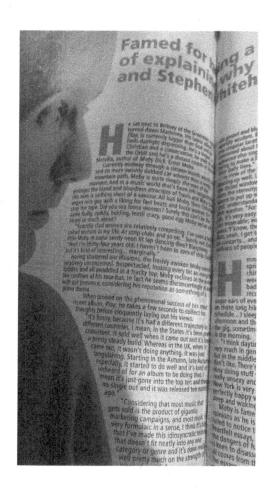

Steve is ahead of me in his size 11 Nikes on the grippy metal steps up to Moby's bus. I clamber up behind him onto the double-decker vehicle, which takes up a whole row of parking spaces outside Leeds Met. I am chuckling to myself as I step over the last shiny fragments of a Stereophonics CD, lobbed from the window and now ground into the tarmac by giant wheels. With the unexpected success of his album *Play* (its songs seem to soundtrack every car advert and TV food show), Moby is at this precise moment the most successful electronic musician on the planet. We write about him turning down Madonna and sitting next to Britney Spears at the Grammy Awards. But as I hoist myself into his cabin, it feels like the star's enormous coach is the story with its luxury sleep pods, on-board cinema and collection of Ali G VHS tapes lined up on a shelf where the singer is settling down onto bean bag-style cushions. We start the interview by trying to get him to say Ali G's catchphrase 'Hear me now!', but he declines politely, rubbing his eye with his left hand.

Moby is very relaxed because he's been asleep all day. He offers us a beer, reaching with an outstretched arm into a large, well-stocked fridge with see-through double doors. Soon I am sinking back into lush upholstery clutching a can of Red Stripe with one hand, holding my slim black dictaphone with the other. Being a music journalist feels like a very good idea indeed. Moby explains why he chooses to snooze from 9 a.m. to 5 p.m. before he gets up to do press a couple of hours before show time. 'I think daytime is kind of distressing,' he says, as we perch opposite, leaning in to hear his soft voice. 'People are running around, busy doing stuff they don't enjoy.' I think for a moment about my sprint to the stamping machine with my Rupert Murdoch essay a few hours ago. One of *Play*'s central songs – 'Why Does My Heart Feel So Bad?' – begins to make more sense. He tells us about the 'miserable jobs' he did in the days before pop stardom, which included washing dishes, working in a shopping mall and cutting grass. I like the smell of grass, I tell him, almost by mistake, as if speaking out loud in a dream. 'Sure,' he replies, smiling at my intervention.

*

The synths at the start of 'Porcelain' sound like rain clouds being pasted into the sky on a palette knife loaded with greys and blues. The notes smoosh and slide, they are heavy with radio static and they gather at the edges with the ghosts of previously lived lives. A downpour might wash them away forever, but in this moment I feel that I could live inside their glistening folds. These back-to-front notes are the string section of US composer Ernest Gold's track 'Fight for Survival'. Moby has put the melody into reverse on his sampler and the result creates a feeling of microscopic time travel. I am a beetle scuttling between 1961 and 1999 through a small tear in a green leaf. I am the ladybird fanning out my tiny, crumpled wings and flying into a future just beyond the trees.

'Porcelain' is the track that I am most obsessed with from *Play* and I switch it to loop on my MiniDisc player as I take another unneeded bus ride on the circular route around Leeds. The song's percussive textures trip over themselves, but softly so, and the intermittent 'Hey' seems resigned and accepting, as pebbles of piano skim across the university lake. 'In my dreams I'm dying all the time,' sings Moby, in a way that sounds almost uplifting. 'I never meant to hurt you, I never meant to lie.' I must tuck this away for the future, because I will need to say these words myself one day. Moby is free, perhaps even flying, over a world of grey buildings, swooshing around hearts that need mending, finding a place to rest on a chimney stack. The strings that wind around him will cushion him – and me, listening, eight times in a row – if he falls. The twinkling middle eight is a sunbeam breaking through a cloud and when I wrap myself inside it, I find I want to step inside his 'kaleidoscopic mind' and see where the sequins really land. I want to know whether the edges of the little mirrors really exist.

*

We spend more than an hour with Moby, asking him questions about drugs ('I don't do them'), veganism ('Compare a plate with grains and fruits and vegetables to a plate with pigs' intestines') and his unexpectedly *Loaded*-esque views on dating ('Women in no clothes, just high heels, are very sexy'). Then we say our farewells and descend from Moby's bus into the real world. It feels strange to exit his cushioned bubble and land back inside a regular Leeds afternoon with its buses queuing up Woodhouse Lane, dirty pigeons and a discarded chicken box somersaulting across the road in the breeze. I look up to see the sun just dipping behind the buildings, a stream of golden light illuminating the side of a building across the empty car park. I look at my shoes as I hop down into the street. Today I'm in my new Red Adidas SL72s and I'm convinced Moby liked them. Steve and I make our way back inside and sit down on the black couch with a relieved sigh. We make a plan to transcribe the interview in chunks. I will write the intro, Steve will form the structure, we'll come up with a fact box. We will watch the show and then reconvene after the gig to start creating our centrespread. Headline: Definitely Moby.

Lucky's pizza shop is less than a mile away from the newspaper office and three minutes from us by delivery bike. We have a special relationship with the staff there and Wednesday night is curry night as we take a break from praying for our floppy discs. Most of the arts teams are in the office – us in music corner tinkering with this week's pages, the book reviewers who emerge sporadically from huge towers of review copies, the film team who are rarely around and various other writers who are late to file their words. Naveed puts in the order for multiple chicken tikkas, a vegetable korma, eight naan breads plus poppadoms and plenty of cans of Dr Pepper, Coke and Lilt. Occasionally we order actual pizza before hunkering down over our computers, waiting for the Lucky's man to ring the buzzer. The curries, when they arrive, always seem suspiciously bright red, but we do not complain because every week this banquet is ours for free. It is a strange coincidence that year on year, our paper announces that Lucky's has been voted the students' favourite takeaway in Leeds.

*

David writes features for *Leeds Student* and whenever he arrives at the office doors, and I am already at my desk working on a piece, a naughty grin spreads across his face. When I see this, I know it is the call sign for an imminent adventure: tonight is going to be fun and quite possibly a tiny bit unhinged. As the office empties out, our thoughts of going home fade into the dark grey clouds beyond the window. David is handsome and funny and makes everyone around him feel better about whatever situation they are in: late with an essay, hungover, still drunk or unsure whether their latest article contains too many jokes about biscuits. We both have the same habit of working well beyond midnight, when the sensible people – the book team and the smiley Clares – have long ago packed up and gone. We are deep into the long, dark nights of the year when this happens again. 'Another all-nighter?' David asks as I turn my head to get a better look at the current status of this week's music pages, which features my review of Suede at Manchester Apollo (Brett Anderson is 'jaggedly hyperactive', Neil Codling is 'feeble looking') and Steve's take on The Herbaliser at the Cockpit ('A little jazz can be a dangerous thing').

David and I pop down to the Metropolitan bar, which is two floors below us via big noisy doors that swing back and forth and remind me of a hospital corridor. We sprint down, taking the steps in twos and threes, just before last orders, so that we can bring our pints back to our desks. It is not *that* Met Bar, but the joke never gets old, and we pretend that we are leading a life of glamour despite the fact we are in jeans and trainers and queuing up for chips, more chips, cider and lager. The paper's new editor, Clare, has left for the day, so we risk balancing our plastic glasses perilously close to the computers on which we are still typing out our pieces for Friday's edition. In the name of creativity, we also split a mysterious tablet that has come our way via David's pigeon hole and wash it down with a sip of Strongbow. We stare at our screens, determined to get our work done, but soon enough David is snorting with laughter and it sets me off. I am trying to resize a black-and-white image of Brett Anderson onstage in Manchester, but Brett keeps turning into Mr Blobby. David is opposite me, and I can just about manage to block my view of him if I sit squarely at my monitor, but he keeps popping his head around to pull faces and shout 'Blobby!' while puffing his cheeks out. This goes on for a while.

He is writing a piece about what our student bedrooms say about us and is naturally being hilarious about the décor snapped by our photographer friend Gilly in random rooms across student Leeds (it's always Brudenell Road, the Hessles and the Harolds). We laugh together at the room with weights on the floor, a *Loaded* poster of Cindy Crawford and a *Thomas the Tank Engine* duvet. Our soundtrack through the night is Radio 1 and, at some point during the small hours, when we fully believe that we are in a state of full creative flow, David secretly sends an email to presenter Scott Mills. Inebriated and high but convinced that we are creating our best work ever, we find that we have at some point drifted from our office swivel chairs to the long, fake-leather seat by the window and now we are staring instead into a cool Leeds night, the city blinking back at us. My chin rests on the cold metal rim that is gathering condensation. David's arm is propped up on the window rest, his fingers holding a Marlboro Red. He says he has given up smoking again, as he throws away the butt. People think I am in love with David, and maybe I am, but I know that he is gay and I love my trips with him to Queens Court, the only gay bar in Leeds and a place where at least I can guarantee hearing a song by the Smiths, or even Morrissey himself, who will soon unknowingly snub me.

As the clock ticks towards 4 a.m., we are listening to an Ibiza set on Mills' show and together we feel peaceful watching glimmers of early-morning sun rise over a city that looks cleaner at this time of day. We are happy to be quiet and still just now, enjoying each other's presence without the need for speech. I don't want to break the spell by moving my legs as I kneel, arms across the windowsill. Our hazy state is interrupted by something else: the sound of our own names being read out.

'This next one is for Anna and David in the *Leeds Student* office,' says Scott. 'They've emailed me to say that they've been awake for so long their eyes are bleeding . . . Err, ok, good luck with the rest of your morning, guys . . .' David and I slide onto the floor laughing. We stay down there for a while among the Lucky's boxes. We try again to do more writing, but decide we've done quite well and deserve a nap on the squashy couch at the other end of the office. What seems like a few minutes later, we hear a familiar voice. 'Good morning, you two. Did you get everything done?' It's our editor, and the answer is no.

*

I take the diagonal route home as the sun rises over the lake next to the Roger Stevens Building, pleased with myself for being awake for the most beautiful part of the day. I am fully aware that I've cheated by pulling an all-nighter, but I walk with a little skip in my step because I am alive and young and lucky to have noticed that this is the case. Two seagulls float serenely through willows, and I don't want to disturb them with my clumsy human ways; my footsteps too loud, the grit beneath my trainers too crunchy, my breath punctuating the rustling sounds of nature that have not yet been taken over by the hiss of car wheels on Woodhouse Lane. But then I also want to greet these nomadic birds and congratulate them on finding such a heavenly spot in the middle of a city.

I smirk as I walk past the EC Stoner building, like everybody does. As I make my way up the cascade of steps next to the main library –

the Edward Boyle with its huge sliding glass doors – I think about Luke Skywalker and the rumour that a scene from *Star Wars* was shot on the Red Route, the sky corridor that floats above my head and connects the upper and lower sweeps of the campus without the need to go outside. We perpetuate the myth and, on rainy days. we like to imagine lightsaber battles taking place between noticeboards pinned with flyers for volleyball club and medieval society.

As I cut into Hyde Park, I am torn between listening to the bird-song in the trees and putting on the song that I have ready to go on my MiniDisc player, 'White Love' by One Dove, which is my current obsession and route one to emotion. I can feel the song's mellow new berries in the path taken by fledglings through the hedges that run along the road's edge. I pass a jogger as I am tasting the bassline along a desire line that winds past the curry house in the middle of the green. The cut-throughs that criss-cross the park seem to fit the beat. A whispered 'wanna hold onto this for you' hangs over the song's dream-like opening bars and I stop to look at water droplets suspended in a spider's web.

I have discovered One Dove only recently after falling in love with singer Dot Allison's heavenly vocals ('pure ecstasy' and a 'bittersweet barrage', I write in a review of her solo album *Afterglow* a few months later), but it's Andy Weatherall's wigged-out production on 1993's *Morning Dove White* that turns a beautiful voice into an intensely emotional listen. I pick up the album from my sister's CD shop on an afternoon of music adventure and it takes me on many journeys of introspection, around the Leeds ring road via outer space. I do not want to share these tunes; they belong in my headphones and in these moments. I feel ahead of the day, blinking inside my own private circle of sun. *Morning Dove White* is a description for the physical world

CONNECTION IS A SONG

I am seeing with tired yet clear all-nighter eyes; a new day that is fresh and dewy, the stamen in its petals untouched, its dusty sugars all for me. I think about Moby sleeping all day and I want to tell him he is missing this.

28

Number one sycophant

My signed copy of *Darkdancer* on CD and the front cover of *Juice* magazine inside *Leeds Student*.

Jacques Lu Cont is bouncing up and down in a white jump suit, his pink cropped hair lit up by lights that move across the stage in frantic circles. I am on the front row pushed against the metal barrier, my arms reaching into an orange haze across the security pit as I try to catch Jacques' eye and send him a look. I am hoping he will glance back in my direction and see that I am the girl to whom he has just promised his disco outfit, but he is fully immersed in executing his moves as '(Hey You) What's that Sound?' pumps across our bobbing heads. The crowd shifts and slides with the hyperactive beat, all of us dreaming we are at a 1985 roller disco and skating backwards with complete confidence while stylishly chewing gum. I lose my place, but I really don't mind. As the bassline pushes me back into the dancing swirl, the track's looping guitars pull me forwards again to be disco-buffeted back to the spot where I began. My feet skid across the smooth floor of Leeds Met as I try unsuccessfully to catch my breath.

The crowd ripples in this bubblegum state for a while before Lu Cont (real name Stuart Price) vanishes in a fog of dry ice, then re-appears for the encore flanked by his two dancers, also dressed all in white. The trio rotate flawlessly – and with a Butlins intensity – around two keyboards as the stage fans out like a wide grin. I feel a strange kind of pride that Les Rythmes Digitales are being loved so much tonight; I had thought that they were still my secret. A couple of hours ago, I think they were.

'Tiffany! *The Dukes of Hazard*! England winning at cricket!' I write as I put together my article for the middle pages of *Juice*, trying to remember what it was that I actually liked about growing up in the 1980s. I describe the album, *Darkdancer*, as a 'secret slice of teary-eyed nostalgia tucked behind the fake leather sofa of your mind'. When I sit down to interview him in the bright white room backstage, Lu Cont is very much on board with my pre-gig chatter and accepts that his songs do come quite close to pastiching the things that lit up the previous decade: keyboards, stuttering samples and middle eights that flash like neon. 'Hypnotise' barely disguises its nod to the Eurythmics, 'Sometimes' features vocals by Nik Kershaw and 'Take a Little Time' wears sequinned fingerless gloves in its homage to *Desperately Seeking Susan*-era Madonna.[i]

I tell Jacques about the day I met the Human League's Phil Oakey as a two-year-old and he leans in to hear more. I explain that my memory of seeing his asymmetric fringe appear along our suburban driveway is now so hard-baked into my brain that it feels like it really did happen (his brother was our parents' neighbour in Headingley, so it *is* possible), and Lu Cont agrees that this half dream of unprovable nostalgia fits the addictive fakeness of the era – the mood that he is trying to recreate using drum machines and samples and motorway lights painted in acrylic. His aim, he says, is to be unapologetically mainstream and at this point I check that my Dictaphone is still rolling, while also taking feverish notes in biro, because I really do want him to succeed – and to possibly destroy the likes of Steps in the process. This talking point has me asking what led to the song 'Jacques Your Body (Make Me Sweat)' being featured in a TV promo campaign for a soft drink. 'The Sunny Delight advert was the perfect example of a product that was so firmly rooted in the masses of record-buying public,' he explains, 'and it kind of made the perfect connection in my head to have this [drink] that was bought by every single pop music lover and link it to me.'

The show feels like an aerobics class set to all these familiar childhood sounds and I smile to myself as I dance because I am the band's 'number one sycophant'. This is what Lu Cont writes in black marker pen on my CD copy of the album after I have declared

---

[i] Lu Cont will later produce Madonna for real on 2005's *Confessions on a Dance Floor*. It is clear that I gave him the idea, but he never gets in touch to say thanks.

myself a fan, but one that does not want to be 'too sycophantic'. Jacques grins and promises to gift me his white boiler suit at some future undisclosed date. As it seems clear he is a time traveller, I accept the offer without pinning him down to a decade.

*

I bump into Sonja from the newspaper as I walk over the DJ Shadow bridge into town. She greets me with a broad smile and asks what I'm listening to on my headphones. 'Les Rythmes Digitales. Do you know them?' She nods and before I know it, we are deep in conversation about the way certain music can remind you of a very specific childhood memory. I tell her that even though I am a new student in Leeds, I am actually from Leeds and that by walking around these streets and suburbs, I am both cementing and overwriting distant memories of cycling in the Hollies on sun-bleached days in the mid-'80s and that in those moments I am still building up to asking Nanny Olive for a Fruit Polo, which she will fish out from a pocket of hairpins and tissues. Sonja and I end up standing on the bridge for an hour, the grey traffic whooshing beneath us, talking about music and all the things that music makes us feel and do. There is a connection that feels – again – like time travel and I sense that I have already been friends with Sonja for years. Together we invent imaginary 'shooty pens' that, we say, will allow us to write ideas on the ceiling from a stationary position in bed. This way, we will be able to put together music reviews as we lie down, thinking, possibly dozing, and we will never again forget the storyline of an important dream – or a great question we plan to ask the Sneaker Pimps or a Welshman who is staring at his shoes with their green and orange trim.

*

I am still working out what just happened in my conversation with Gruff Rhys from the Super Furry Animals in a room above Leeds Town and Country Club. He looks longingly at his trainers throughout, only once meeting my eye. He is not unfriendly, but he seems sleepy and declares that he loves his shoes so much that he wants to put them on his mantelpiece. As a trainer lover, who today is in astronaut-ish white Velcro Pumas, I initially think *Well, I can work with this*, but the struggle to engage him becomes concerning as his voice keeps slowing down and trailing away. It dawns on me that Gruff might be ever so slightly and absolutely definitely stoned. Eventually he is activated by a discussion about chart music, when I mention that his band have only brushed the top twenty twice.

'Shit music is very important because, without it, you couldn't define what good music is,' he tells me as he ponders the neat stripes along his shoes, stopping briefly to tell me again how much he loves them. I ask him about the Welsh scene that has taken shape around the Super Furries, the Manic Street Preachers and Catatonia. 'We're not in a band because we're Welsh. We're in a band because we love music, melodies and frequencies,' he says with more purpose, stroking the side of his right foot. We agree to disagree on the Stereophonics who are 'nice people who do what they do', but when he lifts his head at the end of the interview, he says something about sport and music that I ask him to repeat, because – as a (now secret) football fan – I've never thought about it this way before. 'Music brings people together. That's the beauty of it. Sport divides people. At a football match, half the people hate the other half, but at a gig everyone's on the same side.'

In my tan-coloured airline bag, I have the first Super Furry Animals CD I ever bought, but in the end I don't pull it out because it no longer feels right to ask him to sign it. We are equals in trainer worship. He is sweet and polite, wishing me good luck in assembling my piece, before shuffling off through a door back to his dressing room, still rubbing his eyes, and still looking at his feet.

'First time, I did it for the hell of it / Stuck it on the back of my tongue and swallowed it,' sings Gruff on 'Something 4 the Weekend', a single that has been in my collection for two years, bought from George Heapy's in Knaresborough and a song that seems to be all about taking drugs. It is from the album *Fuzzy Logic*, which always makes me think once again (just like *Moon Safari*) of 1980s kids' TV show, *Button Moon*. I imagine rockets made from felt and cardboard tubes taking off from tissue-paper launchpads, and I'm fascinated by the way Gruff sings 'gerrin' easier'. It is almost a Yorkshire accent but, of course, it is not, and I vanish again with him, and his Adidas trainers, to a place where recorders and flutes soundtrack shining stars that, on closer inspection, are made only by pinprick holes in a black curtain.

*

Not all interviews are equal, and my *Leeds Student* music journalism career is about to take an awkward turn. I had imagined myself breezing into Morrissey's dressing room and finding a way of putting him at ease, perhaps with a chat about teapots or his favourite *Coronation Street* character. Instead, I am listening to a muffled version of 'November Spawned a Monster' through the back doors of the Town and Country Club. I look down at my feet and see that my Puma trainers are blotchy with rain as I stand too close to a puddle floating with cigarette butts. I let out a sigh and pull up the zip under my chin. The giant doors squeak; they are padlocked but loose. Each gust of air prizes me a little more hope, and just enough to keep trying to listen. Rose is with me for a bit, but then she eye rolls, exhales and leaves, muttering something about Morrissey being a has-been anyway. I am still wounded by rejection and decide to stick it out for a bit longer. Perhaps his people will relent and let me in.

A few hours ago, right here, I had watched a flurry of activity as black instrument cases covered in stickers were brought inside by the star's roadies in black t-shirts and jeans. But now it's just me here and I've been banned from entry, along with all other writers. Morrissey says he doesn't want any journalists in tonight, and that includes reporters from *Leeds Student*. Eventually, because I'm cold and wet, I give up on holding my left ear against the door and I follow Rose home. After a plate of Super Noodles, I lie back on my single bed, still with the floral duvet given to me by Mum, and use the shooty pens to write words around my orangey lamp. I put on the Smiths to make myself feel worse. I contemplate what I will do instead of my review for this Friday's music pages[ii] – a piece about

---

[ii] Standing in the rain, feeling bitter, I begin to regret my preview from the week before (*Leeds Student*, 5 November, 1999): 'Morrissey returns from obscurity (his mum's Manchester Barratt home) today, bringing his genial combination of gloom-laden eloquence and Wildean wit to Leeds Town and Country. The reason for this tour remains as enigmatic as Steven Patrick himself. He may be 'devious and truculent' (so said a High Court judge) and a bit of a loner with a penchant for gladioli and National Health specs, but we still love him. Let's hope November spawns a monster performance from King Moz.'

being cross with Morrissey? – but I wake up the next morning and realise that my heart is not in it. We shall meet Morrissey's snub with silence, I declare, again with the shooty pens. I think about Moby's beer and Jacques' jumpsuit – still unclaimed, but somewhere out there in the *Button Moon* sky, *mine*. Morrissey, a fading star behind a black curtain, should have been glad of our attention.

29

Take the bomp

On my first motorbike, a Vespa ET2, which I called Tiffany after the '80s singer. Yes, I am checking my eyeliner in the wing mirror.

Inside my hot head there is a darkening fuzz. The music feels far away. I find myself in a moment that I did not think would ever happen as I listen to a song that was born in the melting embers of the last century. 'Deceptacon' – an electro-punk tune downloaded from Napster – gave me a shove and bundled me here and it never stopped to ask if I was ok.

The song is often there – in the background of a TV show, on the decks as I pay the cloakroom attendant, on another mixtape – but it rattles around me, escaping my full attention, as I pack up my things ready to leave Leeds. I lie on the grass one last time in the park at Woodhouse Moor, near the tree where I first heard the Strokes, and stare up at the gently receding sun beyond the curry house. I wander through the campus, no longer with an essay under my arm, and throw a two-pence piece into the Roger Stevens lake for the last time; watching the little grey circles until they are absolutely gone. I am not ready to go. But 'Deceptacon' has other plans.

The song finally, truly, connects but not until the new century.

I am at a gig and passing out in a frantic kind of slow-motion; my legs gently buckling, my knees no longer doing the job of being knees. In this distant jelly-ish world, my thoughts roll around like marbles along mauve and yellow plastic tunnels. I am awake but not truly here. I can hear 'Deceptacon' as if through a wall in another room, and I am trying to cling onto its cartoon texture as the people around me shimmer away into pastel-coloured fractals. I know I am gone, and I promise the room, with its sweaty walls and moving plimsole floors, that I will be back. 'Who took the bomp?' screams singer Kathleen Hanna with all her lungs. I took the bomp, I tell her in my head, and now I'm bomping to the floor. 'See you later,' says Hanna and – yes – I take it personally. Not for the first time, I have fainted at a gig.

It happens at the Manic Street Preachers when I am sixteen, it happens at Death in Vegas in the third year at Leeds (I'm annoyed to learn that I drop both my bottle of beer and Marlboro Light during the descent) and now it is happening again as Le Tigre's 1999 riot girl anthem turns the dance floor into a throbbing mass of bodies that together generate the heat of the sun with a backdraught of solar flares. For the moment, I have lost contact with the universe, and all of this is taking place inside a tiny club up winding stairs to what feels like someone's front room.

When I finally come round, I find a small, wobbly cup of water precariously wedged between my fingers. My hand feels too weak to form a proper grip as I lift the plastic container, but the cool liquid is heavenly on my lips. My head has turned into folded paper again and I have that fretful feeling – still with me since the Doncaster Dome 'Motorcycle Emptiness' episode – that I have spent many minutes in darkness and missed the best bit of the song. This is funny because the song has no best bit; 'Deceptacon' is one continuous blast of electro-punk and it never lets up.

By 1999, Le Tigre's singer, formerly of Bikini Kill, is a seasoned veteran of the feminist-activist-punk-zine scene. Hanna has long since found her way into grunge and punk through spoken-word performances that take on themes from domestic violence to sexism. I am only learning this when I realise that she also gave Kurt Cobain his most famous line when she daubed 'Kurt smells like teen spirit' (Teen Spirit was a deodorant marketed at teenage girls) on the Nirvana frontman's bedroom wall during a drinking session. By the end of the decade, Hanna has moved to New York and, as the next century dawns, her new band Le Tigre are at the centre of the 'punk feminist electronic' genre. 'Wanna disco? Wanna see me disco? Let me hear you depoliticise my rhyme,' howls Hanna on 'Deceptacon'. Still political, but now danceable, she and her bandmates lay the ground with disco grenades that I will try to walk across in my all-new millennial trainers: slip-on Dunlop Green Flash with fake laces. When the bombs blow, a new genre is born: electroclash – the first alternative music movement of the 2000s.

But I am just trying to stand up.

*

Bis share similar anarcho-pop DNA to Le Tigre, but the two bands arrive at my door in very different parts of the decade. Bis catch me in my hungry mid-'90s acquisitions phase, when I am hoovering up intelligence on the indie bands that seem to be flicking ice-pop V-signs at the mainstream. In 1996, they become the first unsigned group to appear on *Top of the Pops*, with their weird little electro-punk anthem 'Kandy Pop', and I watch them bouncing up and down with confused awe. Singer Manda Rin, in her blue dress and hair slide, is just eighteen and only a year older than me. If they can do it, perhaps music has actually changed forever. Everybody's worried about the millennium bug but I'm secretly hoping that everything does actually break. My friend, a new Lisa, one with beautiful intense eyes and a tongue piercing, says that I am 'taut like lace' and I think she means that I need to be easier on myself, and who I am becoming. She has guessed before me that I am in love with a girl. I have spent the third year in Leeds entranced by a new Bernard, one who loves Nina Simone but not me. I need the millennium bug to wipe my head, not just the 2:50 a.m. text messages on my flip phone.

'Sugar sugar kandy pop, push it down and pull it up,' sings Manda on the tune that seems to be an ode to the Push Pop, a craze among our younger siblings that involves licking a candy lipstick inside a plastic cylinder. 'I got better things to do than hang around with you and you,' it continues, and it's exactly how I am feeling too. Bis help make the Britpop scene less Union Jack-ish, bringing their pick 'n' mix fanzine mood to a party where the boys in cagoules are still hogging the kitchen.

My block B friend Debbie plays the Scottish trio on her show on Leeds Student Radio, in between doing impressions of her mum. Debbie is another Lupton Flats comrade and together we have made serious inroads into the cultural scene of Leeds University. Debbie plays guitar – she dazzles me with the revelation that she was actually *in* cult Brighton band Electrelane – and in her room she has the green screen-printed poster for Birdie's *Some Dusty* on the wall. Birdie is really Debsey from Saint Etienne and, as anyone who knows knows, is the shimmering dancing heart of my favourite band. This shared fandom seals the deal on our friendship, and we go on to interview bands for LSR, including a mesmerising evening watching Trish Keenan from Broadcast do her vocal exercises in the back of the Duchess pub. She uses a cassette recorder just like the ones you see being clicked into action to grill suspects in TV police dramas set in the 1970s.

*

Back in the hot little room, five years in the future, I am still recovering from fainting during 'Deceptacon'. My girlfriend puts her cool porcelain hand across my forehead. I'm not dreaming, I say slowly to myself, this is real life and it's my life. I look back at her and smile with fuzzy gratitude, still unsure if I have fully escaped the marble labyrinth inside my head. We sit together on orange plastic school-style chairs in a corridor with a view across a Victorian street that is criss-crossed with telegraph wires. She looks at me with kind eyes and waits for a while longer for me to say if I feel better. Half an hour passes like this before we edge carefully back to the dancing room to see what is happening. The room pulses with electronic sounds and I see dozens of girls dancing together in couples. I feel happy to be one of them.

It seems a while since talk of Bernard.

30

2 a.m. eternal

Wandering through a drum 'n' bass night, unaware that a rare photographic moment is happening inside a club in the era before camera phones.

I am not meant to be a raver, but I wake up one morning in 1999 to find that I am. The Orbit in Morley, in a pair of bouncing chemical shoes; a circle of sweaty dancers, one of them me, at Judge Jules in Preston with skydiving Emma; a glimpse of velvet inside a coach and horses that only my eyes can see along a dawn motorway. Later I will know the drill: a text message just after midnight, a taxi ride with strangers, an unexpected gesture of acceptance from the rozzers, and a field in Bedfordshire where a queue forms at 2 a.m. at the hatch on the side of an ice-cream van.

On its little doors, that fan out along brass hinges, I look for the sugary pinks of a strawberry Mini Milk or Mivvi but see instead the flecked purple of Northern Lights and something called a Mitsubishi. I live in a state of gentle fascination inside these strange hours of rambling adventure, travelling through houses with stairs that lead to upside-down sofas, climbing through gaps in the wall and then flopping onto a mattress scattered in ash.

I talk with a boy called Joe for a while, mostly about music. He loves the Sabres of Paradise, so I take my Andy Weatherall cue and tell him about the bird-filled hedgerows of One Dove. He looks up from the mattress and smiles. Soon enough he is kissing me with ruby-stained lips, but then he stops almost comically, to explain that he drinks red wine strategically 'to take the edge off the speed'. It keeps him balanced, he says. Joe says he's read my music reviews in *Leeds Student*, which fills me with brief terror (I'd never imagined *real* readers), but then I drift back into the haze of the present and we stare together at the wallpaper: little red tulips circled by green leaves that very nearly line up along the join. I turn my attention to the muffled noises of people moving through the bubble-hum of the DIY comedown room and I hear familiar voices that somehow seem unreachable. When the sun appears at the window, I walk home down empty Leeds streets, my steps like Mr Soft in the Trebor Softmints advert: spaced out and detached, along the pavements my granny would know so well. I am always time travelling and in this moment I really want to ask her for a Fruit Polo.

*

A little while later I am queuing to get into a techno night with Steve. For now it is just us, but we will meet our group of friends inside and they will greet us like fellow members of a covert resistance movement: a nod of recognition and a quick exchange. We edge forwards with that nervous feeling that precedes a big night; the anticipation of an expedition laced with a creeping dread that one of us won't get in. When all this voluntary tension is done with, I know that I will go wandering – my favourite clubbing solo sport – but I have no idea yet that I will meet a girl, whose name I will never know, and she will give me a slow and beautiful hand massage. As ever, I am nervous about looking too young – it is always me being pulled out of line and asked to prove my age. In front of me is a boy in a KLF t-shirt that I take as a good omen. I try to chat to him, but he too is in the arrivals zone and cannot relax while the door staff inspect us under bright lights. We are all aboard and bound for Mu Mu Land, but not quite yet. When my turn comes, the back of my hand is stamped with a small blue orb and I glide in freely, abroad on the wrong side of Leeds.

*

I had never really understood the KLF, but I knew that they connected my early forays into pop music – reading *Smash Hits* under the fading light of the loft window – with the luminescent world of Bedfordshire raves that I would later find over the farm gate and beyond the dip in the field. I remember sitting in baffled amazement at their performance at the 1992 Brit Awards, watching with my sisters in the living room on the TV set with the silver-grey oblong buttons. Dad pulls a face that says 'modern music has gone to the dogs' as a rogue version of '3 a.m. Eternal' booms out with ear-bleeding accompaniment from another band – Who are they? Why are they here? – called Extreme Noise Terror. Fake gunshots rain over a stunned audience and some of them appear to flinch. 'This is television freedom,' snarls Bill Drummond as Mum sets down a pot of tea on the table by the fire. I move my head so as not to miss any fragment of this weird spectacle. A blue police light flashes and guitars crunch into a sound that I think must be death metal. I have no idea what is going on and yet in the same part of this space-time brain explosion – just adjacent to the chaos – we will be watching Beverley Craven sing the soothing ballad 'Promise Me' in her purple floaty jacket, perched on a piano stool, surrounded by softly rotating half-moons of light. Mum will say she quite likes the song as we splutter our distress ('But she's so uncool!'). When the KLF open the show it is like nothing that has gone before. Dad walks away in baffled disgust, as ever with a tea towel over his arm. Bill Drummond, the frontman, fires a machine gun into the crowd, and I duck even though I am watching from far away in Yorkshire. We sisters look at each other with horror but when we realise it's a stunt, Claire turns to me with a grin.

Just as I was not meant to be a raver, the KLF were not meant to be loved by pop fans like me. The duo are masters of the unhinged afterparty but they end up in my *Smash Hits* with Big Fun on the cover seemingly by mistake, and therefore entirely deliberately. Bill Drummond and Jimmy Cauty set themselves the task of creating several hit records in a row in 1991, eight years before I am listening to them through the wall at a house party. The two songs to actually emerge from this plan are 'What Time Is Love?' and '3 a.m. Eternal', which both contain the blueprint of the chart-rave boom. Thinly veiled drug references are everywhere and soon the Shamen will be shouting, under the guise of 'Ebeneezer Goode', 'E's are good!' into the nation's living rooms while we blow onto our dangerously hot Findus Crispy Pancakes. Our parents don't seem to notice the code words (Mum is more interested in the faux-Dickensian dancer in a top hat), but we do ('Has anybody got any Veras?' – 'Vera Lynns are skins or Rizla papers, you know, for making roll-up cigarettes, Dad.'). The KLF's mad mix of performance art and hyper-productive nihilism lays the foundations for these odd moments. It's a perfect embodiment of '90s culture in which a gawping audience (us on the settee, one minute startled, the next eye rolling), pop music, money and inverted desire for success form part of the same caffeinated scrapbook.

'The KLF, aha ah aha aha' becomes the inky stamp on the doorway to every big night out, but not until I am well on my way to being a near grown-up. '3 a.m. Eternal' dances around me until I understand its true powers via the look that is exchanged between my best friends, deep into the night. Steve is doing his carrot-picking dance. Rose is looking up at the lights, a cigarette in her outstretched hand. Marion is smiling and circling her own elegantly dangling wrist. 'It's 3 a.m., 3 a.m., 3 a.m. eternal' and everyone's arms are in the air, an upwards human tree, sweat running down our necks and most of us accidental ravers.

*

I'm in an imaginary field staring at green summer leaves in a bright blue sky. It is deep into a pulsing techno night as the fake sun comes up. Around us, twinkling lights, like glimmering stars occasionally unsighted in the sea of limbs. Up ahead, an orb blinks through television foliage. 'Born Slippy' is the song and it seems to take on ever more epic qualities over these times that seem to be in fast-forward. It's not the lyrics, it's the neon blue *feeling* of the track. In sixth form, we were obsessed with both the song and *Trainspotting*, the Danny Boyle film on which it most famously features, watching the movie repeatedly in instalments on our friends' parents' VHS players in spare rooms, huddled under assorted childhood duvets. We watched again and again, learning the lines. 'Hey, Rent Boy, you bring me down a fuckin' smoke.'

Already in a state of nostalgia for the first encounter, I find that the neon greenery has shifted from view, and I am blinded by a mess of strobes as I try to find my friends in the criss-crossed darkness. I listen, as if not in my own body, as 'Born Slippy' enters its feverish second phase, my feverish second phase. *Let my feelings slip.* Watching from the future, I send myself a message through the blue-grey triangles of the duvet. My upper body feels warm but my legs are free as they slide along your cool hips, my arms propped on two pillows. Through the gaps in the fabric, I see tiny beads of sweat on your shoulders, the curve of your breast interrupted by the edge of the bed frame.

2 A.M. ETERNAL

In my head I can always hear a song.

I look at your skin and the folds might be verses, and so I swim to meet your chorus. A tummy rumbles and I don't know if it's mine or yours. I hear 'Born Slippy' like a pulse, the song, here, again, finally making true sense: those chords that connected me to myself, now connecting me to you. Through forests of brambles, conveyor belts in wines shops and through brackish waters in which I once believed I could not swim, I find the route; my toes sweep close to stones on the seabed, but never scraping as I had so long feared. The song pulls me to the water's surface and very close to a salty kiss with the girl I have been trying for so long to find.

*

Most regular club nights end at 2 a.m. and, just before this happens, after the KLF and Underworld, there is only one song. A month after the release of '3 a.m. Eternal', in the grey February of 1991, Massive Attack deliver a tune that will become the soundtrack of the decade. I don't know it for a long time, but it is the central puzzle piece of my 1990s. 'Unfinished Sympathy'. Its unfinished-ness is the doorway that connects the different versions of me. A circling loop, back through the house: on one side Nanny's view of the car wash in suburbia, on the other the fairy lights of my unfurling adult life. As the song's opening bars skitter across another Leeds dancefloor, I consider again how strange it is that it has existed in the world all this time.

'Unfinished Sympathy' sneaks into the UK charts at number fifty-one on 23 February 1991 under the name 'Massive' (the band briefly drop 'Attack' during the 1991 Gulf War) and climbs to number thirteen. The song never reaches the top ten where The Simpsons are doing the Bartman, and comedy duo Hale & Pace are stonking for Comic Relief. In my plastic red nose, I am unaware that the track is destiny-bound to find me again a while from now. But there it is on *Top of the Pops*, next to Jason Donovan and Colour Me Badd.

'You really hurt me, baby' are the words at the source of the spring that flows into most of pop's rivers, it seems that it is our fundamental need to set feelings of love and loss to music and then stand helpless in their icy spray. This is where I choose to be as the decade that has taken me from childhood to the *start of everything* begins its furious journey under bridges, around foaming bends and over rocks towards the sea. Like a twig racing in a fast current, I choose to be thrown around and battered by oncoming obstacles. At last, I want it all to happen.

It is the simplicity of Shara Nelson's mournful lyric that flushes the veins of the song as she describes a lover who has 'really cut me'. A mystery figure holds the 'curiousness of your potential kiss', and it is this phrase that floods my mind with emotion as I perch along the edges of my friends' emerging relationships. I am the willowy stick, briefly held up along the edge of the riverbank. I am standing, alone, looking at whirlpools of dancing heads in silvery blue. Steve is falling in love with the girl from Speed Queen. Marion is going out with the boy I once thought owned the perfect record collection. Rose is with the singer in shiny trousers from the band that sounds like My Life Story. David has the attention of Queens Court as I watch from dusty shadows. *I know that I've imagined love before.*

Shara Nelson's vocal is cushioned by a percussive sample lifted from bebop musician JJ Johnson's 'Parade Strut' that forms the underbelly of the song while orchestral strings rise above its deep waters. These are so expensive to record, at Abbey Road Studios in London, that Massive Attack are forced to sell the band's shared car, a Mitsubishi Shogun, to fund the session. A Mitsubishi for sale, again, I smile to myself, as I hang my arms over a Victorian rail, gazing into the crowd. Together the beat and the violins create an atmosphere of foreboding and hope, which suits me just fine in my saucer-eyed state of solo contemplation. The 'Hey-ay, hey hey-ah, hey, ay ay' sample, borrowed from John McLaughlin and the Mahavishnu Orchestra's 'Planetary Citizen' is the primal yelp that sees the track – and me – finally snap out of a dream. I drink lemonade and it is the very finest lemonade that has passed my lips since the Bentley Rhythm Ace hydration. A further beehive of samples and a spiritual, hypnotic tinkling bell – the song's pivotal motif (from a jazz cover of Paul Simon's 'Take Me to the Mardi Gras') – drive the song to its hard-to-bear emotional peak and from here, 'Unfinished Sympathy' follows me over road and rail, through house parties, via ill-conceived 2 a.m. text messages to the rawness of falling in love again and an eyelash brushing my cheek. I play the song probably hundreds of times on my MiniDisc player; riding the bus, walking alone, always seeking and often finding a new connection. Listening is like peeling back the wallpaper in a beautiful old house: the swirls and layers, endless and infinite patterns, the incomplete fingerprints of previous inhabitants. I don't mind at all that I will never find the beginning.

Shara Nelson is captured in a single continuous shot as she strides through the golden-brown light of an LA afternoon. It is chaotic and serene all at once, and I often re-enact the video on journeys past the fish market and up to the station in Leeds. Both the song and Nelson's walk are a monument to the act of living in your head as life unspools. She walks past a second-hand furniture store, across traffic intersections and beyond a car parts shop. She overtakes hairy bikers, street drinkers and lonely shoppers. A loved-up couple embrace on the sidewalk and a group of teenage girls start a fruit fight. Like me on my night walks, Nelson is in her own universe, a spirit moving between worlds. We lose her at Norma's Beauty Salon.

On the balcony where I am standing and still trying to pick out my friends in the crowd, I decide that 'Unfinished Sympathy' is the best song of the 1990s. It is the track from the beginning of the decade that finds me at the end (which is, of course, the beginning). I declare that it can only ever be the night's final tune and the sound of eternal 2 a.m.s. Its epic beauty is the resolution to all that has gone before, the last doorway to imagination before the lights reveal that the sea I have been swimming in is really an ocean of plastic cups. 'Come home with me,' says a boy with Oasis hair. 'I've got beers and condoms.' 'No thanks,' I reply, before making my way past the kebab van and into my private blue night. I look for my friends but they are dispersed now, finding their own way. And in one continuous shot, I watch myself walk home.

Afterword

It is only through song that I have been able to recall the adventures that I experienced with the people in this book. Where memory had become black and white, the music brought back vivid colours, like an old paint palette splashed with water after years in the attic. My parents set the scene with their shared love of music, Dad especially with his large vinyl collection, some of which sits at the back of the garage in North Yorkshire. Mum and Dad still live in the Victorian house with the Virginia creeper growing up the wall, but when I visit Mum no longer rings a school bell to call me down for dinner.

My sister Claire remains the biggest Pulp fan in the UK, very probably. I have finally returned to her the cassette copy of Saint Etienne's 'Who Do You Think You Are' that I 'borrowed' for three decades and found only recently in a dusty Dunlop Green Flash box. To my younger sibling Kerstin, I apologise sincerely for hacking your Swan Keyper and I am grateful that you still keep me on my toes with new songs.

Lisa, I loved those early evenings in your bedroom, and I'm glad the 30-year-old in-jokes still make us laugh whenever we message. Yorkie, you may not have realised how important those nights in the blue Mini were to me, and so I hope that you know now. Hélène, you were wise ahead of your time by choosing Radio 4 and Jarvis, and I'm so happy we always keep in touch.

Mr Robinson, I have tried several times to find you to say thanks for both the music and the words. I hope you might read this. If not, I'll be on the bridge where you used to sit with Poz, dangling my feet into the water, one earphone each.

Steve, you have never stopped being very tall, and you still own many pairs of trainers, thank you for dragging me to that meeting with the *Leeds Student* music editors. Rose, I'm not sure you ever believed I forgot your name for a whole week, but now it's in writing I hope it makes more sense. Debbie, you were always my musical compass and remain so now, especially when we do that dance. Marion, you continue to connect our friendship circle from over the sea, but did you ever hand in your essay? Clare and Naveed, my *Leeds Student* newspaper editors, thank you for letting me compare so many bands to biscuits and for setting me on this path in the first place. David, I saw you on the train that time and you had the same mischievous look in your eye. Sonja, you remain my felt-tip pen adviser on life as well as music. Adam, my route into town from our flat was *definitely* the fastest.

The girl with the porcelain hands at the Le Tigre disco is Liza, with whom I spent eighteen years and share a wonderful daughter, Frankie, who – incidentally – has seriously cool music taste.

Discography

There are many songs that connect this book, its people and its moments: each one a little marker in the dot-to-dot puzzle of another time and place. But the beauty of music is that it waits for you. What is irreversibly associated with *that time* for one person is the beginning of a fresh new era to another. This playlist is the sound of someone else's teens, but, quite possibly, the soundtrack to your train journey on Tuesday and maybe even your greatest love story. Put these songs on in your bedroom, fling open the windows, climb the lamppost and let them be your guide.

Music is a fizzing reminder of the past but, truly, music is for now.

Sinéad O'Connor – 'Nothing Compares 2 U'
They Might Be Giants – 'Birdhouse in Your Soul'
Candy Flip – 'Strawberry Fields Forever'
ENGLANDneworder – 'World in Motion'
EMF – 'Unbelievable'
Cocteau Twins – 'Heaven or Las Vegas'
Chesney Hawkes – 'The One and Only'
Orbital – 'Halcyon and On and On'
Take That – 'Once You've Tasted Love'
Shakespears Sister – 'Stay'

CONNECTION IS A SONG

East 17 – 'Deep'
Madonna – 'Vogue'
Saint Etienne – 'Who Do You Think You Are'
Blur – 'Girls & Boys'
Oasis – 'Live Forever'
Menswear – 'Daydreamer'
Space – 'Neighbourhood'
Catatonia – 'Lost Cat'
Geneva – 'Into the Blue'
Utah Saints – 'Something Good'
Manic Street Preachers – 'Little Baby Nothing'
Garbage – 'Milk'
Mansun – 'Wide Open Space'
McAlmont & Butler – 'Yes'
Spice Girls – 'Wannabe'
The Chemical Brothers – 'Leave Home'
The Stone Roses – 'I Am the Resurrection'
Radiohead – 'Just'
No Doubt – 'Don't Speak'
Belle and Sebastian – 'The State I Am In'
Gay Dad – 'To Earth with Love'
Mazzy Star – 'Fade Into You'
Stina Nordenstam – 'Little Star'
White Town – 'Your Woman'
Cornershop – 'Brimful of Asha'
The Verve – 'Bitter Sweet Symphony'
Morrissey – 'Hold On to Your Friends'
Elastica – 'Connection'
Suede – 'Trash'
Portishead – 'Sour Times'
Dubstar – 'Stars'

DISCOGRAPHY

Air – 'Kelly Watch the Stars'

Stereolab – 'French Disko'

Primal Scream – 'Don't Fight It, Feel It'

Pulp – 'Common People'

Bentley Rhythm Ace – 'Bentley's Gonna Sort You Out'

Boards of Canada – 'Roygbiv'

Gene – 'Fighting Fit'

My Life Story – '12 Reasons Why I Love Her'

ATB – '9 P.M. (Till I Come)'

DJ Shadow – 'Midnight in a Perfect World'

Moby – 'Porcelain'

One Dove – 'White Love'

Les Rythmes Digitales – '(Hey You) What's that Sound?'

Super Furry Animals – 'Something 4 the Weekend'

Le Tigre – 'Deceptacon'

Bis – 'Kandy Pop'

The KLF – '3 a.m. Eternal'

Underworld – 'Born Slippy'

Massive Attack – 'Unfinished Sympathy'

These songs are listed in the order they appear in the book. To listen to Anna's playlist, scan this code inside the Spotify app:

https://open.spotify.com/playlist/2cisTiExOhctDJwcmBfjRe

Acknowledgements

Special thanks to Pete Selby at Nine Eight for helping this mad dream come true and to Bob Stanley from my favourite band, Saint Etienne, who made me believe in magic. Thank you to Nige Tassell and James Lilford for the precision editing. Thanks hugely to Mark Rusher who saw my jigsaw pieces and helped me find the edges, to Jenny Parrott for the Zoom call that inspired me to get started and to Matthew Hamilton for being my guiding hand. Deep gratitude to Liza Brett for all the support over all the years. Thank you to Andrew Doble, my dad, for the beautiful poem at the start of the book, and to my mum, Rosemary Doble, who never stops rooting for me. Love and thanks to my sisters: to Claire Doble, who started all this with her *Smash Hits* sticker album, and to Kerstin Doble who still makes me laugh like no other.

And to Laura Ansell: thank you – you showed me that music never stops connecting me to new, wonderful times.